THE QUALITY OF MURDER

The Quality of Murder

A psychiatric and legal evaluation of motives and responsibilities involved in the plea of insanity as revealed in outstanding murder cases of this century.

JOHN HOLLAND CASSITY, M.D.
Psychiatrist-in-Charge of Criminal Service, Bellevue Hospital, New York

Introduction by JAMES D. C. MURRAY

The Julian Press, Inc., New York 1958

Published by the Julian Press, Inc.
80 East 11th Street, New York 3

Library of Congress Catalog Card Number 58–9815
Manufactured in the United States of America
by H. Wolff, New York
DESIGN: *Marshall Lee*

TO MY WIFE, AND CO-WORKER, CLAIRE

I wish to express my gratitude to Dr. Salvatore Cutolo, Assistant Superintendent of Bellevue Hospital and to Mr. William Ettel, Chief of Public Relations for the Department of Hospitals, for the necessary official clearance from the City of New York.

I am also indebted to Judge Samuel S. Leibowitz of the Kings County Court, who was kind enough to lend me the minutes in the Pisanti case, and to Assistant District Attorneys Vincent Dermody and Karl Grebow as well as to Mr. Joseph J. Hennessey, Court Stenographer at the Court of General Sessions.

My thanks and appreciation to my friend, Mr. George Carroll, newspaper editor who gave me many stimulating suggestions regarding the preparation of the manuscript; to Mrs. Betty Groman, the Secretary of our Female Criminal Service at Bellevue Hospital who typed my original and final manuscript; and to Mr. Michael Fetta, Secretary of the Male Division of the Criminal Service at Bellevue Hospital who aided me considerably in gathering material in the Guiteau case at the New York Public Library.

Introduction

A NOTED PSYCHIATRIST, John Holland Cassity, M.D., Psychiatrist-in-Charge of the Criminal Service in the Psychiatric Department of New York's huge Bellevue Hospital, in his book, THE QUALITY OF MURDER, has thrown open the door to some startling revelations regarding the psychopathology of homicide.

Since 1940, Dr. Cassity has studied thousands accused of crime and sent by Court order for him to ascertain whether they were mentally responsible, under the rules of law, for their homicidal acts. Through his testimony, in company with other doctors, when a plea of insanity was interposed in a homicide prosecution, men died in the electric chair; others, declared insane, were committed to the Criminal Insane Asylum, in Beacon, New York, buried behind its walls where society buries its civil dead.

Strangely enough, one finds in his book, Dr. Cassity's opinion that man is a potential killer. Witness the flood of television scenes in which there are villains and killings and there lurks a suspicion that the eager viewer of the scenes in his own mind and fancy favors the killer. Happily for society, these homicidal thoughts are seldom translated into action.

The public, horrified by the killings on the public streets and other places in metropolitan districts, has become psychologically and psychiatrically conscious. Rarely does an edition of the public press fail to carry stories of youthful gangs, reminiscent of Tartar tribes, roaming the streets bent on causelessly decimating each other, and often succeeding in the effort. People are looking for the cause and the prevention, unsuccessfully. Possibly, they might find a clue in Dr. Cassity's book.

THE QUALITY OF MURDER is intriguing and interesting not only to the medical profession and the legal profession but to the layman as well. Every pattern of mental illness is found in the cases he has so thoroughly studied and documented. This book is unique by reason of the fact that it contains verbatim stenographic reports out of the mouths of the accused and witnesses and doctors.

Through the book parades a long procession of killers with innocent blood on their hands. Among many other cases is found the Court report of the trial of Guiteau, who fatally shot President Garfield, in 1881, in a railroad station, in the District of Columbia. The so-called psychiatrist who testified for the prosecution in the Guiteau murder case presented a most bizarre testimony. This doctor attributed the homicidal tendencies of the defendant to certain protuberances on his head. One could readily conceive that the same character of protuberance might be found on the head of the Judge who presided at the trial and the jurors who rendered their verdict and, possibly, the lawyers who prosecuted the indictment. Dr.

Cassity observes that psychiatry was in its infancy in 1881.

The killing of the noted architect Stanford White by Harry Thaw, the scion of a millionaire Pittsburgh family, in 1906, was a cause celebre. In the first trial, Thaw was defended by a lawyer named Delphin M. Delmas, imported from California, who coined the phrase "Dementia Americana," in pleading the unwritten law.

In this book one also finds a discerning and complete Court report of the case of Leopold and Loeb, who tortured little Bobby Franks to death. It was defense counsel Clarence Darrow's masterpiece, in which he demonstrated that he had a keener knowledge of mental processes than did the prosecution doctors.

Also in his book, Dr. Cassity found the apparent mental abnormality that impelled beautiful sixteen-year-old Lena Nienstedt to sever a tailor's head almost completely from his body, in Queens County, Long Island.

The most intriguing and mystifying case in the history of psychiatry is fully documented from Court records when Chester B. Duryea was released from Matteawan State Criminal Asylum. He had been an inmate of that institution for virtually a quarter of a century. For over fifteen years of that time he was a Rip Van Winkle, with apparently no conscious perceptions of reality. This case is a classic, in that after all those years his mind found itself.

And you have the John Roche case, the unconscionable killer of both men and women. The book recites the revolting butchery and rape of a little fourteen-year-old girl on her way to school with her books and her lunch lying beside her as she bled to death on the floor of a hallway. Roche has died in the electric chair. As one of his assigned lawyers I interpose a personal note. In spite of all the murder cases I have defended, when the Medical Examiner was testifying as to the wounds that brought death to the little girl, I could not listen to him and had to leave the courtroom, so deeply was I affected by the fate of this innocent child.

As one reads the book one finds it more interesting, though horrifying, than fabricated fiction.

Dr. Cassity, along with the majority of psychiatrists who are called upon by the State to make examinations and findings in criminal cases, is concerned with the rule of law that governs criminal prosecutions as it now appears in the statute books. The anomaly of the law is that one may be medically insane and yet legally sane. England, in 1843, formulated a rule of law in the M'Naughten case to determine if an accused was legally liable for a criminal act. Dr. Cassity's book, while somewhat technical in this respect, suggests a change in the law which will be more adequate and precise in determining abnormal mental conditions in criminal cases.

The anomaly in the law, at least in the minds of some judges, can be found in the case of George Metesky, who was named the "Mad Bomber." He exploded home-made bombs in lockers, telephone booths and theaters. Arraigned before one New York Judge, the Court disregarded the findings of Bellevue psychiatrists that Metesky was not in a mental condition to be tried. In a similar indictment found against Metesky in Kings County, which is across the bridge from New York County, a noted Judge held to the contrary and sent Metesky to Matteawan State Criminal Insane Asylum, where he is now confined. Apparently, the first Judge decided the issue because of the evidence that Metesky competently manufactured home-made bombs and eluded detection for a long time. Metesky was a quiet, congenial man who wrote and spoke precise English. He harbored a grudge against a utility company, in which he entertained the fixation that it had wronged him. The twist in his mind appeared in that he planted bombs where innocent people might be maimed or killed, without any disclosure that he performed the acts in retaliation against the utility company. His claim was that he was doing it for the benefit of society, and yet he could not explain how injury to innocent people could be of any service to society. The noted County Judge of Kings County, Samuel S. Leibowitz, far ahead of others, stated that this was a medical case and not a legal one.

Dr. Cassity has an impressive background in psychiatric medicine which qualifies him as an expert in his field. A graduate of Tulane University, he trained in famed Saint Elizabeth's Hospital in Washington, D.C., under Dr. W. A. White, one of the world's most noted psychiatrists. Later, he became a Fellow in the National Committee for Mental Hygiene, and was Director of the Mental Hygiene Clinic for the State of New Jersey.

Lawyer as I am, possibly the book is more interesting

and instructive to me than it might be to the man in the street, but I am of the opinion that he, too, will be interested, in view of the so-called national crime wave that currently overwhelms our country.

James D. C. Murray

New York City
September, 1958

Contents

1 Yesterday's law and today's psychiatry

THE URGE to murder fellow human beings, either singly or collectively, has been apparent in man's behavior since the advent of recorded history. The Homeric legends of the *Iliad* and *Odyssey* as well as the Chronicles of the Old Testament are replete with accounts of what appear to be relatively senseless personal killings and mass massacres. This general idea is further substantiated by the predatory performances of Ghengis Khan and Attila, and later by the ruthless executions and beheadings ordered, at slight or no provocation, usually the latter, by early French and English monarchs. The man-to-man homicides were punished by death or forgotten, depending upon the whim of the kings. If the murderer had courted royal favor, his act might result in an advance in social or economic status. Otherwise—quick dispatch!

Though the incidence of murder continues, the self-preservation instinct of the individual has become more involved with that of his neighbor. On such a basis, a new means of coping with the destruction of life has emerged. Moral and ethical barriers have been erected by society to resist the urge to murder and thus to save itself and its own structure. Society has decreed that murderous acts are against the will of the majority. If perpetrated, these acts are punishable by prolonged incarceration or even by death.

Our legal patterns have served as a deterrent to murder. They have, by no means, however, eradicated the desire to kill. Nor have they entirely eliminated the incidence of murder.

A number of sociologists in the field have attributed the many murders in our present-day culture to predominantly economic factors. The disproportionate emphasis on the possession and importance of money seems sometimes to goad people of small scruples and intelligence into acts of murder. When apprehended in the course of a robbery, they proceed to the next step. They have come prepared, in the event of frustration, to kill.

Other sociologists—and students of psychology—have pointed to our recent World Wars as environments where the murderous tendencies of the human being have been exposed to stimuli too powerful to shun or to sublimate. They have called the result a mass frenzy or mob hysteria. They have also admitted that, though the madness of a dictator may be an established fact, there is no conceivable way of demonstrating the insanity of the millions who made possible the ignominies incited by him.

The killer urge is evidently present on a mass basis in our peacetime society, as well, however. In Gangsterdom, U.S.A., murder is accepted as part and parcel of the business code. And outside of Gangsterdom, the tough killer seems to be more generally envied and admired than pitied or despised. Movies, television plays, radio programs, even books featuring these characters enjoy enormous popularity. Absorbed, today's reading or listening audience obviously identifies itself with the villain or the hero, either or both of whom may be a killer.

The tragic conclusion we must come to is that the potential to kill exists in people. Normally, it is curbed by our laws. And the laws are such as to help develop in the public mind the moral sense of right and wrong.

But what of those acts of impulse, the murders of the moment, the results of sudden uncontrollable feelings of anger, affront, passion, when the moral sense of right and wrong is completely forgotten? Do such moments occurring in a usually normal person absolve him of the responsibility for his act? In my opinion, they do not. I believe that this kind of murderer should stand trial and be judged. The psychiatrist, as well as the prosecuting attorney, is working towards the goal of protecting society from the incursions made against its comparatively fragile means of strengthening the legal—and moral—foundations on which civilization builds and survives. It is only the murderer mentally ill to the extent that he cannot appreciate the nature of his act who should be exonerated—and this with a stipulation that he be institutionalized pending recovery.

I have long had the conviction that the general public should have access to information regarding the function and weight of psychiatric opinion in criminal cases, particularly those of major consequence, as well as a better idea about the laws which are meant to serve as safeguards for their social well-being. It is my belief that a well informed public is less inclined to be stampeded into supporting laws which may have outlived their productive purpose and more apt, instead, to participate in helping to bring into existence new laws which can better serve modern social needs.

To my knowledge, no similar information has been published until now. Weihofen's "Insanity as a Defense in Crime" as well as "The Urge to Punish" deal almost exclusively with legal interpretations of the M'Naughten Rules as construed in the various states here in the United States. Weihofen was not a psychiatrist nor was he attempting to write from a psychiatric angle. The M'Naughten Rules contain no psychiatric criteria for judgment. In 1843, when they were formulated, psychiatry had not yet been developed as a disciplined medical area. The legal criteria which the Rules present are still, however, the most important in the United States, Great Britain, and its dominions.

Dr. Davidson, who was a psychiatrist, wrote a book entitled "Forensic Psychiatry" concerned principally with the intricacies encountered in court proceedings by the mental expert. Dr. Wertham, my former colleague and associate, wrote "Show of Violence" which dealt primarily with a few cases he had seen at Bellevue in the 1930's. While his efforts were indeed creditable, the treatise did not encompass, even fractionally, the field of murder in the sense that I wish to do in this book. Viewing the subject retrospectively, this will be the first attempt to follow through, chronologically, the concept of mental disorder as a defense plea to avoid capital punishment for the crime of murder.

I have been a personal participant in all of the cases, with the exception of those occurring before 1940, that I shall discuss in this book. In the earlier cases, specifically those of Guiteau, Thaw, Duryea, and Loeb-Leopold, I have made use of the authentic historical background of each culprit, including the trial minutes, extracts of which I will quote in the discussion.

What I am actually presenting is a behind the scenes description of what goes on in psychiatric dealings and trials concerning people charged with murder in the first degree when a plea of insanity is involved. The reader will discover, as he goes along, what appear to be basic conflicts between the psychiatric expert and the prosecuting attorney. The former usually contends that the culprit is "incapable of understanding the charges preferred against him and is unable to make an adequate defense for himself." The latter, citing Section 1120 of the Penal Code, State of New York, an off-shoot of the old M'Naughten Rule, insists that the defendant "knew what he was doing at the time of the act." At times, psychiatric expert and prosecuting attorney disagree so sharply, the conflicts seem irreconcilable. This is not really so. In the main, both psychiatrist and prosecutor are carefully listening to each other and continually being affected by whatever new understanding is projected into the situation. Both, as I have noted before, are functioning towards the same purpose, the better protection of society.

Regardless of how right a psychiatrist may seem in a

particular case, it is fortunate that the prosecuting attorney is there to challenge him. The new laws that the psychiatrist, by his very plea, is helping to advance must be subjected to the most careful scrutiny. It is important that new laws emerge constantly but these new laws must be an improvement over existing legislation. Once a law becomes a fact, its ability to operate needs to be more than theoretical. Only then is it capable of fulfilling the purpose for which it was designed—the further safeguarding of society. And as society advances, it becomes more and more evident that the purpose of law is not so much punitive as it is preventative.

For his part, the psychiatrist who specializes in legal cases must always be open to the fuller implications of what the existing laws demand so that he may meet this challenge on a basis that is truly equal to the social responsibilities involved.

In a current case, that is, a case being tried at the time of this writing, a District Attorney in Brooklyn is opposing me with considerable vigor. The case is one of acid-throwing, not of homicide. In this instance, the District Attorney wants and demands conviction despite the fact that the defendant, age 17, has shown anti-social and assaultive tendencies since the age of 8 or 9. The prosecuting attorney, doing his duty as he sees it, has in his possession an amplitude of evidence pointing to the guilt of the defendant, all of which is denied by the latter, incidentally. I, as a psychiatrist, am prepared to testify that the accused is irresponsible because of mental aberrations dating back to childhood. The main point of divergence between the District Attorney and myself is one of perspective. He sees a situation in cross-section; I survey it longitudinally. He may be unduly influenced by hide-bound and antiquated legal precepts, and I may be unduly swayed by my fervor for the furtherance of psychiatric progress in the criminal field.

And with my point of view I offer a further thought: A young person prosecuted only on criminal charges and not given the benefit of psychiatric treatment, is eligible after having served his sentence—possibly at the end of a year or two—to return to society where he may perform similar or even more violent acts. In most cases, the person who is tried and committed on the basis of mental illness is removed from society for a considerably longer period. His return, predicated as it is on improvement in mental health, is then, in my opinion, less likely to be a threat to society.

No lawyer, psychiatrist, or jurist is adamant in his opinion, however. All of us are amenable to conclusions derived from reasonable discussion. Yet, we are all hampered by decadent laws written generations ago. Can these be changed? Some authorities seem to think so.

On January 28, 1956, Mr. Justice William O. Douglas delivered an address at the Annual Commencement of the William Alanson White Institute in New York City. He opened it as follows:

"Recent developments in the law should hearten psychiatrists that their pleas do not always fall upon deaf ears. I refer particularly to the celebrated case of Durham versus the United States, decided July 1, 1954, by the

Court of Appeals for the District of Columbia. The Court, in an imaginative opinion by Judge Baselon, rejected the long-established 'right and wrong' and 'irresistible impulse' tests of insanity as a defense in criminal cases, and announced as a new test that . . . our accused is not criminally responsible if his unlawful act was the product of mental disease or mental defect. To most psychiatrists this was a break with tradition that was long overdue."

The "right and wrong" tests to which Justice Douglas refers are criteria contained in the M'Naughten Rules of 1843. A murderer's ability to distinguish right from wrong at the time of the act is still a principal means of determining his sanity and criminal responsibility.

Justice Douglas comments further:

Under the Durham test, the psychiatrist gives any relevant testimony; and he speaks to the Court and the Jury in the language of his discipline. He is at last free to advise the court and the jury concerning the totality of the accused's personality and condition. No longer is he forced to divide a person up into a rational being and an emotional one, to divorce his conscious and his unconscious state, or to separate the knowing part of the mind from the willing part, or the feeling part. The Durham case does, indeed, invite examination of all the facts of the total personality—the cognitive, the volitional and the emotional.

. . . Under the Durham Rule no one theory of psychiatry is turned into a principle of law. The psychiatrist

will be free to present his testimony about the mental condition of the accused in concepts that are familiar to him and medically realistic. . . .

The Judge himself is realistic when he says:

Hospitalization of the dangerous may lay as heavy a hand on the victim as life imprisonment. . . . And in the days ahead there will doubtless be many contests in habeas corpus proceedings over the legality of a detention based upon a particular psychiatric opinion. . . . But these are necessary perplexities of the new system . . . which gets on with the problem of the criminal and the sick. The regime of the Durham test will offer exciting opportunities for men and women from medicine, psychiatry and law.

Professor Weihofen also rejects the M'Naughten criteria in "The Urge to Murder." In the chapter, "Two Roads from M'Naughten," he says:

Thoughtful students of the subject have today come largely around to the view that the right and wrong test is not the clear and certain formula it was supposed to be and that certainly it is, at all events, a wild goose that we may as well give up chasing. There is no clear and simple rule for making discriminations that are inherently complex and difficult.

Proponents of the right and wrong test today largely accept this fact and have made an interesting shift in their position. In place of the old argument that the traditional test is clear and definite, they now tell us that—

rightly understood—it is broad enough to cover all cases that should properly be covered.

. . . The most engagingly frank statement of this view is that of a British psychiatrist: "To put it in a rather bald way, the present rules are such nonsense in many cases, that the people can exercise their own common sense, whereas with more precise rules more rigidly interpreted, the ultimate effect would not be as good as the present one."

But many, and probably most of us, would prefer Mr. Justice Frankfurter's position that, "If you find rules that are, broadly speaking, discredited by those who administer them . . . then I think the law serves its best interests by trying to be more honest about it . . . to have rules which cannot rationally be justified, except by a process of misinterpretation which distorts and often practically nullifies them . . . is not a desirable system. . . . I am a great believer in being as candid as possible about my institutions. They are in a large measure abandoned in practice, and therefore I think the M'Naughten Rules are in a large measure shams. That is a very strong word, but I think the M'Naughten Rules are very difficult for conscientious people and not difficult enough for people who say, "We'll just juggle them."

Professor Weihofen also mentions that the Royal Commission on Capital Punishment in England (1953) has recommended a rule similar to that established in the Durham case a year later. He likewise calls attention to the fact that the American Law Institute has been drafting "a herculean undertaking" that has been in progress for a number of years now. At the 1955 meeting of the Institute, tentative draft sections dealing with mental responsibility were discussed and approved.

Without laying claim to any prophetic vision, I nevertheless venture to predict that the future belongs to two alternatives. We are going to depart from the M'Naughten test or try to find our way toward a rule that better accords with better modern psychiatric thinking. The eminence of the staff and the committee that has been working on the Model Penal Code . . . has been such that . . . when it is finally promulgated, is certain to be accepted as the definitive model for all criminal law reforms in years to come.

The Model Code's main provision dealing with mental irresponsibility, as tentatively approved by the Institute, reads as follows:

"A person is not responsible for criminal conduct if, at the time of such conduct, as a result of mental disease or defect, he lacks substantial capacity either to appreciate the criminality of his conduct or to conform his conduct to the requirements of the law."

Admittedly this is an improvement on the M'Naughten Rule which seems to require *total* impairment of cognitive faculty: the defendant must not "know"—hence, recognize or take cognizance of his criminal behavior.

A major hitch in both M'Naughten and the "Model"

Codes is that no psychiatric help is made available within a reasonable time after the act is committed. The accused may have been an alcoholic, epileptic, recurrent schizophrenic, manic-depressive, or suffering from none of these conditions. The point is that we cannot testify with assuredness without being present soon after the crime is committed. From our later examinations and historical accounts we can only piece things together and come up with little more than a speculative answer.

The Medical Examiner's Department is covered by a group of doctors who are available at all hours. If a murder is committed, they are on hand shortly thereafter to conduct a preliminary survey and, later, a detailed pathological examination. In our Psychiatric Department, we are quite frequently required to wait from one to four weeks before we can even see the accused. By that time the picture may well have changed. For example:

Had I seen the "Mad Dog Killers," described in a later chapter, on the day of the murders or shortly thereafter, I could have recognized immediately that they were not suffering from a major mental disorder. That they had planned and perpetrated the payroll stickup, was never debatable. The problem was whether or not they had preconceived ideas of murder. They carried lethal weapons as a device of threat in obtaining the loot. Their murder of the payroll bearer and of the police officer were acts of frenzied defense. Yet, almost immediately following the crimes, both killers became mute, simultaneously! I had no opportunity to examine them for several days. My task was then to determine: Were they psychopaths, psychotics, or simply complete fakers?

Another example is that of the man who incurred a head injury in line of work on the docks of New York. He committed murder, apparently while in a dazed state. I did not see him for several months. It was only then that I heard the history from his relatives and from his attorney, whom he did not even recognize at our Formal Hearing. Had I known the facts, I certainly could have evaluated the case far more quickly.

Much needs to be done if we are to achieve any substantial effectiveness in handling our murder cases.

Much is already being done:

Governor Averell Harriman of New York has recently appointed a Committee to study potential substitutions for the M'Naughten Rules, while at the same time preserving safeguards against looseness.

Judge Samuel Leibowitz in two cases of attempted murder—the "Mad Bomber Case" and the case of the "Acid Thrower"—has expressed an opinion that may well mean much for the future. There is "no such thing as legal insanity," he has said. ". . . that is a medical problem."

2

Murder and mental responsibility

Perhaps there has been no instance in the civilized world where combined with such universal sympathy for the victim, there has been so little feeling for the doer of the foul deed as in this . . . (—a chronicler of the trial of Charles J. Guiteau, assassin of President Garfield, quoted in Vincent Towne's Unsolved Mysteries.)

JOURNAL-AMERICAN, 1/19/36

IN SHAW'S PLAY, "Major Barbara," the millionaire character, Underschaft, is worried about his son Stephen's career. Stephen has announced that he is not interested in politics, drama, or in any of the professions. "Well," his father asks, "is there anything you know or care for?" To this, the son replies, "I know the difference between right and wrong." Amused, the father makes the following retort: "You don't say so! What! No capacity for business, no knowledge of law, no sympathy for art, no pretension to philosophy; only a simple knowledge of the secret that has puzzled all the philosophers, baffled all the lawyers, muddled all the men of business, and ruined most of the artists: The secret of right and wrong. Why, man, you are a genius, a master of masters, a god! At twenty-four, too."

A murderer's ability to know right from wrong is still the principal criterion by which we judge his sanity in our courts of law today. And like Mr. Shaw's character, I wish to register my objections. Such a test is not an adequate measuring rod for determining mental responsibility in murder cases.

In psychiatric understanding, we have come a long way

from the days when mental derangement was not even taken into consideration in our thinking about murder. Prior to 1800, murder was regarded either as a machination of the devil or rationalized as completely justifiable. The diabolical antics of Henry VIII, for example, were accepted as his royal prerogative and condoned accordingly.

In the year 1800, the specific issue of exoneration by reason of insanity was raised for the first time. Hadfield, a British war veteran, previously discharged by the Army on the grounds of "madness," had made an attempt to kill King George III. In previous capital cases, authorities had required "total deprivation of memory to protect a man from criminal responsibility." The memory of this defendant was not only unimpaired but, on the contrary, extremely clear. He gave a lucid account both of his very well-recollected attempt on the Monarch's life and of his reason for the act. It seems that, like the Savior, he was to sacrifice himself for the salvation of the world. He fired point-blank at His Majesty in order to fulfill his destiny and go to his "reward." Just how this could be achieved by doing away with the King, the defendant failed to specify. The defense counsel, Lord Erskine, described the delusions to which his client was subject as "so terrific as to overpower the faculties." Hadfield was acquitted but one Judge stated, "What the legal test of responsibility was is not clear and was not an adoption of delusion as a test in the place of the knowledge of right from wrong."

This opinion, in essence requiring the criminal to be able to know right from wrong, served as a precedent which still lingers to haunt us. The concept of right and wrong, in our world, seems to vary widely, differing cultures developing different standards of ethics, both for individuals and groups. Even murder, in a mass sense, is exculpated in totalitarian states, on the basis of political exigency, and, as I have already mentioned, in our own gangsterdom, on the grounds of business expediency. A plea of "not guilty by reason of insanity" in such instances would be palpably ludicrous.

Twelve years after the Hadfield trial, a defendant named Bellingham, suffering from the fantasy that the government owed him large sums of money, shot and killed the treasury official who had refused him satisfaction. In this case, the Judge and jury ignored the delusional factor as having any bearing upon the defendant's ability to distinguish between right and wrong. Bellingham was executed.

In 1840, a man called Oxford was tried for firing a shot at Queen Victoria. His action was motivated by a vague persuasion that the Crown was perpetrating a plot against him, this despite the fact that he was a relatively nondescript and unknown person. It was in this case that the phrase "Nature and quality of the act" was coined. Lord Chief Justice Denman, addressing the jury, summarized, "The question is whether the prisoner was laboring under a species of insanity which satisfies you that he was quite unaware of the nature, character and consequences of the act he was committing and unconscious of it being a crime." Oxford was absolved of guilt on the grounds of mental derangement.

This interpretation was adopted by the judiciary panel following the celebrated M'Naughten case three years later. The opinion is still cited as a supplement to the "right and wrong" test. The term "irresistible impulse" was also suggested by the M'Naughten panel.

It was in the heated debate of England's House of Lords, following the M'Naughten case, that the M'Naughten Rules were actually adopted. Daniel M'Naughten, a Civil servant, planning to kill Sir Robert Peel, shot and killed Peel's secretary, Drummond, whom he mistook for Sir Robert. M'Naughten labored under the delusion that enemies were hounding him, Sir Robert Peel being one of the chief enemies. On the basis of insanity, M'Naughten was found "not guilty." The verdict states that he was affected by morbid delusions "which carried him beyond the power of his own control."

But the House of Lords disputed the decision. Members of that body argued back and forth the issue as to whether unsoundness of mind should be permitted to excuse a felony of this sort. It was finally decided to appoint a panel of fifteen Judges whose opinion would be accepted in this case and as a guide for the future.

Three main points are contained in the opinion which we now familiarly refer to as the M'Naughten Rules:

1. The ability to distinguish right from wrong at the time of the specific act.

2. The nature and quality of the act.

3. That even though the defendant is the victim of delusion, if said delusion be separate from and not di-

rectly connected with the criminal act, he is still responsible. This is alluded to as partial insanity.

Psychiatric concepts were not sufficiently developed at the time the M'Naughten Rules were formulated. But these rules are still followed by our legal institutions. The contributions of today's psychiatric knowledge are quietly overlooked or neglected.

The first American murder case to receive consideration in its medical aspects was that of Charles J. Guiteau, who assassinated President Garfield in 1881. The account of the act by the then Secretary of State, James G. Blaine, who was a personal witness to it, is distinctly revealing. The following statement was made on the stand at the trial. The excerpts are taken from the recorded minutes. They are as follows:

On the night of July first, I was engaged until nearly midnight with the President on public business. Upon parting with him, he suggested that I had better call and see him in the morning before he left Washington, because there might be some matters to which he desired to direct my attention. I went to the White House on the morning of Saturday, July the second, in response to this suggestion of the President, reaching there at nine o'clock, or not later than three minutes past nine. I was detained some little time in conference with the President in the cabinet room, and then started with him to the depot. He rode in the carriage in which I went to the White House. His own carriage, in which were his sons, under the conduct of Col. Rockwell, followed. We rode down the avenue with no particular incident and at a moderate speed. On reaching the depot, at the B Street side—the ladies' entrance I think it is called—we sat for a moment and finished the subject upon which we were conversing. After this, the President turned around to say good-bye to me, and I said, "No, I will escort you to the train." I said some little pleasant thing to him to the effect that I did not think it was proper for a President to go unattended—or something of the sort. "I will escort you to the train; and besides, I wish to see the gentlemen of the Cabinet who are going to leave with you." On arriving at the depot, the carriage being a coupe, he necessarily got out first, his side being next to the pavement. As we descended the steps, he turned to the left. He turned to speak to someone, I believe a police officer. While walking through the ladies' waiting room, without any premonition whatever, there was a loud report of a pistol discharge, followed in a very brief interval by a second shot.

At the instant when I first heard the report it occurred to me that it was occasioned by some trouble between persons with whom we were in no way related; that some sudden deed of violence was being committed, and I touched the President as though to hurry him on to get out of it. I thought there might be some danger to his person and to my own being there if there were stray bullets flying around. Just as I did that, the President threw up his hands and said, "My God, what is this?" There was then a rush past me of a man on my right. I followed after *him instinctively. I remember that I stopped just outside the door that leads from the ladies' waiting room, when I heard a shout, "We've got him." . . . In the upper room of the depot, there was a gathering of Cabinet Ministers. There had yet been no report at all of who fired the shots, but I gave the information that the man I saw running, whom I went after and whom I saw the police take was Charles Guiteau.*

Mr. Blaine recognized him instantly as the man who was a crank and had been making a nuisance of himself at the White House. Guiteau had seemed to be obsessed with the idea that he should be appointed to an Ambassadorship to one of the European countries. He had said that he was ready to settle for Paris or Vienna. Though Guiteau had never held any office of consequence and had no political connections, he repeatedly besieged the President and Mr. Blaine with threatening letters and objectionable personal appearances. He had been ejected, finally, from the White House. During the trial, he referred repeatedly to close affiliations with the Civil War General, Sherman, and with two ex-Presidents, Grant and Arthur. They would support him in his claims, he said. Naturally, none of the three offered to do so.

A résumé of the testimony in this trial highlights some of the perplexities encountered while attempting to apply the M'Naughten Rules as a yardstick in reaching a just verdict.

The prosecution contended that the crime was deliberate and premeditated. In support of this claim, it produced three statements written by the defendant prior to the assassination. The first one was dated May 23, 1881, and was addressed to President Garfield. It read as follows: "I have been trying to be your friend. I do not know whether you appreciate it or not, but I am moved to call your attention to a letter from Mr. Blaine, which shows that he is a wicked man, and that if you don't demand his resignation, both you and the Republican party will come to grief." The second one was found among Guiteau's personal papers in his living quarters, labelled, "For Publication." It was dated June 16, 1881, and stated: "I conceived the idea of removing the President four weeks ago. I want my office; Mr. Blaine stands in my way." Exactly two weeks before the murder, which occurred on July 2, 1881, Guiteau made the following notation in his diary:

Washington, Saturday evening, June 18, 1881.

"I intended to remove the President this morning at the depot as he took the cars for Long Branch, but Mrs. Garfield looked so thin, and clung so tenderly to the President's arm, my heart failed me to part them, and I decided to take him alone. It will be no worse for Mrs. Garfield to part with her husband this way than by natural death."

The government thereafter produced an array of witnesses, including hotel clerks, relatives and chance acquaintances, who attested to the fact that Guiteau was a "petty chiseller" and a "dead-beat." The prosecution made the most of this testimony, trying to show that Guiteau possessed a sufficient degree of understanding to know a "soft touch" when he saw one. Hence, argued the Prosecutor, he knew full well what he was doing at the time he killed the President and did so as an act of revenge for the refusal of the President to appoint him to a European Consulship! And, the Prosecutor concluded, it was only after the act was perpetrated that he started feigning insanity.

The defense cited instances wherein the defendant had exhibited very definite signs of mental aberration, demonstrated that some of these had been noticeable over a period of fifteen years before the tragedy occurred. For example, he wrote a letter to his father on April 10th, 1865, seventeen years preceding the crime, which began as follows: "I came to New York in obedience to what I believed to be the call of God for the purpose of pursuing an independent course of theological investigation. . . . And here it is proper to state that the energies of my life are now, and have been for a month, pledged to extend the sovereignty of Jesus Christ, and placing at His disposal a powerful daily paper. I am persuaded that Theocratic presses are destined in due time to supersede pulpit oratory. There are hundreds of thousands of ministers in the world, but not a single Theocratic press. . . . My paper would be a reconciler. It would reconcile the conflicting interests of individuals, of classes, of churches, and of States and Nations . . . I am nevertheless constrained to confess the truth about myself. Therefore I say boldly that I claim inspiration. I claim that I am in the employ of Jesus Christ and Co."

Guiteau's attorney asked him what his idea was in establishing a Theocratic paper. He replied, "The idea was to establish a great organ of the Deity, in this world, as nearly as I can express it, to supersede the Churches and Christian Associations. . . . I proposed to dig them all up and try to rebuild them all over." He then mentioned that it was his destiny to be President.

Despite all this evidence, the District Attorney insisted that Guiteau was simulating in regard to his understanding at the time of the crime. The Prosecutor's contention was supported by several prominent medical witnesses.

The testimony supplied by the medical witnesses of the defense often bordered on the ridiculous. One doctor, a phrenologist, drew elaborate diagrams to show that certain protuberances in the defendant's skull could account for his homicidal tendencies. Another one diagnosed his case as general paresis, despite the fact that there were no diagnostic criteria of brain syphilis at that time. A third medical expert took the stand and testified that he thought Mr. Guiteau was in a state of delirium tremens at the time of the assassination. Delirium tremens, we know today, occurs only in chronic and habitual alcoholics. The defendant was neither. But psychiatry was, in Guiteau's day, only in its infancy. . . .

From the point of view of modern psychiatry, however, I am firmly convinced that Guiteau was insane, both before and at the time of the crime, for the following reasons:

1. Statements obtained from relatives, acquaintances, and even from his fellow attorneys, indicated that his thinking had been erratic, distorted, and illogical for many years before he saw President Garfield.

2. The historical accounts also revealed that he had displayed egotistical and grandiose ideas about his ability, completely out of line with his capacity, either socially or professionally.

3. The fact that he, a small-time lawyer and debt-collector, rejected assistance from the attorneys assigned to him and insisted upon being his own defense counsel demonstrated further his grandiose thinking.

4. His belief that he merited a consulship in Paris or Vienna merely on the grounds that he had written letters to the President supporting his candidacy was definitely obsessive in character.

5. The excerpts from the letter, written in 1865 (quoted earlier), disclose the definite delusional quality of his thought processes, actually an identification with the Deity which would enable him to supersede all religions.

6. Lastly, it is inconceivable that a person could plan a murder and at the same time concoct a story of becoming insane after the act. This Guiteau did not do. During all the months of the trial, he continued to insist that all of his actions were directed by God, on much the same pattern of ideation as that he expressed in the letter to his father in 1865.

So Charles Guiteau was executed by hanging! To me, the account of his testimony and behavior at the trial are proof that he was psychotic both before and after the crime. Had some lesser personage been the victim, the verdict, even then, might have been "not guilty" by reason of insanity.

Charles Guiteau was undoubtedly a common garden variety of paranoid schizophrenia. Not so the other three examples in our early American scene! The facts presented in those cases offer a challenge to psychiatric ingenuity in arriving at diagnostic evaluations, and present legal angles which are indeed unique in the problem of determining mental responsibility.

3 The sinister power of wealth

A special venire of 90 men and 10 women from which a jury will be picked to determine the sanity of Harry K. Thaw, was drawn here today.

JOURNAL-AMERICAN, 3/25/13

IN THE first week of June 1906, Harry K. Thaw, scion of fabulous wealth, shot and killed Stanford White, an internationally known architect. The murder took place on the roof of New York's old Madison Square Garden, on East 26th Street. Thaw, his wife, Evelyn Nesbitt, and White, were there, watching the extravaganza, "Mme. Champagne." White was seated at a table separate from them, nearer the exit. In the middle of the performance, the Thaws decided to leave. Upon passing the architect, Thaw drew a revolver and slew him. Then, he walked calmly to the elevator.

At the trial, Thaw invoked the "unwritten law"—claimed he had been cuckolded by White. He listed perversions and iniquities, allegedly performed by White, in a letter sent to Anthony Comstock, America's crusading moralist. Comstock's fiery indignation soon had a number of the clergy up in arms on Thaw's behalf. A Boston preacher recommended for acquittal on the grounds that Thaw had been defending American womanhood. A play written around the "unwritten law," financed by Thaw money, roused further public sympathy.

The contention of Thaw's attorney seemed to focus on

the idea that the "realization of his wife's infidelity culminated with such force that Thaw became convinced that it was right to kill White." Thaw's mother, eager to conceal the history of psychopathy in her celebrated family, "played down" any possible psychiatric angle.

The result of this trial was a hung jury—7 jurors voting for a first degree murder verdict, and 5 voting against it.

A second trial begun later in the year 1907, ended in January 1908. The dowager mother's attitude was entirely different now. Her ne'er-do-well son's life was at stake. Her purpose now was to prove that Thaw was insane at the time of the murder and had been mentally afflicted since childhood.

Many of the leading psychiatrists in the United States were called in by the defense. Among them were Dr. William A. White, Dr. Smith Ely Jelliffe, Mr. Menas S. Gregory, and Dr. Graeme Hammond.

As far as I can ascertain, the psychiatrists based their conclusions of Thaw's mental incompetency upon pertinent historical facts as well as on personal observations. The information that I have shows that Harry K. Thaw evidenced signs of mental aberration dating back to his childhood. He had tantrums and was unable to adjust emotionally to his surroundings. His mother testified that he was sleepless even as an infant. A childhood tutor stated: "He was excessively nervous . . . frequently subject to outbursts of uncurbed animal passion . . . had St. Vitus Dance and used baby language as late as 7."

At the age of 16, while a student in Wooster University, Thaw's behavior was observed by an instructor, Charles Koehler, to be as follows: "He had a nervous gait . . . walked in a zig-zag manner . . . capacity for concentration weak . . . interpolated mathematical problems with irrelevant questions re games or contests."

As a young adult, according to the testimony of a butler in the Thaw household, Thaw indulged in "pulling the cloth off the breakfast table and booting the meal into the fireplace." More significant, of course, is the fact that on several occasions during his early adulthood, he was placed in private sanitariums in Europe for attempted suicide.

He was admitted to Harvard University but asked to leave very shortly after by President Elliott. The reason was not specified. Reports seem to indicate, however, that it was "for immoral practices."

His mother, testifying further at the trial, stated: "Later on, he would settle into gloom and absent-mindedness. Then he would play Van de Ville music violently. When I asked him what was happening, he would say, 'I can never tell you.' One night, I found him weeping bitterly (he was then past 30). He then told me about some young girl who had been wronged by one of the wickedest men in New York and that even her own mother had not protected her and that he could not overcome his affection for the girl and that he was anxious to wed her. I agreed if her past (her questionable relations with Stanford White) would never be referred to in my house."

Just before the murder, Thaw seemed also to be obsessed by the idea that White was having him followed by thugs. No proof of this, however, was ever adduced or substantiated. Thaw continued only to maintain that the murderous act resulted from "Divine Providence." He had been chosen to be a protector of girls being ravished by perverts.

In my own opinion, Thaw's delusion was nature's method of assuaging his unconscious guilt. A former landlady, from whom he had rented rooms prior to marrying Evelyn, has said this about him:

He rented rooms from me under the name of Professor Reid. He advertised for young girls to train for the stage —ages 15 to 17. He had two whips, one like a riding whip, the other like for a dog. On one occasion, I heard screams of a young girl. Then I saw her partly undressed, neck and limbs covered with welts. I found others writhing from punishment.

According to the landlady, Thaw divided $40,000 among 233 girls. Another girl, known as Mrs. Reid, received $700.

At his second trial, Thaw was declared "not guilty by reason of insanity." In 1908, he was committed to the Matteawan State Hospital for the Criminally Insane.

But in 1913, he was smuggled out of Matteawan in a laundry basket. He fled to Canada. Two years later, he was apprehended in New Hampshire and extradited to New York.

The press was full of the story. Daily newspapers, undoubtedly yielding to pressure from the Thaw family, billed him as a martyr. A writ was finally sustained for his release. Thaw was returned, a free man, to his home in Virginia.

There is no doubt about the fact that Thaw was insane, even before he knew Evelyn or Stanford White. His mother was aware of it though she tried, during the first trial, to conceal her knowledge and to give the impression of being ignorant of the sexual eccentricities in both her son and daughter-in-law. At the second trial, she retained the most competent psychiatrists in the country to prove his insanity and thus save him from the electric chair.

Harry K. Thaw, the free man whom she had succeeded in getting out of Matteawan and back home to her, was still a sick man, however. His mental distortions did not abate. The family never risked allowing him at large without a protective escort. A bodyguard accompanied him. But he continued to make a spectacle of himself in the New York night clubs he frequented.

The Thaw money had managed to return a demented and dangerous man to his community. The unknowing called him a hero. Those close to him knew better. Under inadequate surveillance, he was living out the rest of his days as a problem to himself and to others.

This kind of solution for a person as dangerous as Thaw is unlikely nowadays. Our knowledge of psychiatry has ruled out such unrealistic leniency. Our legal agencies, too, are now more representative of the public interest and less likely to be influenced by private power or wealth. Today, Thaw would have been institutionalized for life. His type of personality disorder does not respond to any presently known psychotherapeutic treatment.

4

A killer understands his crime

Chester B. Duryea, 69, willingly left the drab safety of the Matteawan State Hospital for the Insane yesterday to start a legal battle in Supreme Court, White Plains, which may end in his trial for the murder of his father 25 years ago, and which may send him to his death in the electric chair.

MIRROR, 1/10/40

WHILE THAW was still a fugitive from Matteawan and hiding out in Canada in 1914, another murder, one of the most amazing in the annals of criminal psychiatry, was committed in Brooklyn. Chester B. Duryea, age 45, fired 4 lethal shots into the body of his father at their home on 85th Street, in the Bay Ridge section of Brooklyn, where the two were living alone. They were partners in a chemical manufacturing concern. Friends and relatives reported that their relationship had at all times been amicable. No motive was ever deduced by the authorities to account for the patricide.

A servant in the residence summoned the police. Duryea told a weird story of having been aroused from sleep by figures moving in the next room. He was sure of their identity. They were characters whom he had been instrumental in having convicted on robbery charges when he was acting as Deputy Sheriff, 20 years ago. He had anticipated their revenge. They had warned him that he would "be taken care of" upon the expiration of their sentence. And they had been released only the week before! Thorough investigations regarding these contentions proved that they had no foundation whatsoever in fact.

When informed of his father's death, Duryea became violent. He was placed in mechanical restraints and sent to Bellevue Hospital. Observation there revealed that he was in the throes of an acute psychotic reaction requiring not only the continuance of seclusion, but forced feeding as well.

A Commission was selected by the Court to pass upon his mental condition. The Commission decided that he was a suitable case for commitment to Matteawan.

A study of causative factors disclosed that Duryea had for many years been a periodic alcoholic. On a number of occasions, he had developed delirium tremens, requiring hospitalization in several sanitariums. He had also taken the Keeley Cure, a remedy for severe alcoholics popular in the first decade of the century. He had gone, too, to Muldoon's, the upstate New York farm, where drinkers went to "work it off."

During the week preceding the crime, Duryea had evidently been on an alcoholic binge. The "sneak attack" by marauders was strictly imaginary. It would seem that his father was shot as a result of an illusory state of mind which had caused a misidentity. Duryea had simply mistaken his father for one of his hallucinated assassins.

While this state of thinking is frequently observed in episodes of alcoholic mental derangement, it is exceedingly rare that the condition becomes as semi-permanently persistent as in Duryea's case. Usually, the attendant hallucinatory state is relatively transitory in character. When it endures over months or years, it is almost inevitably a signal of irretrievable brain damage. This condition, known medically as the Korsakoff syndrome, is characterized by confusion in ideation, confabulation (falsification of memory), misidentification of the facts and of individuals, and a tendency to cling to false conceptions conceived originally during an acute paranoid hallucinatory state following a prolonged alcoholic episode. The prognosis in this type of reaction is unpredictable. It depends entirely upon the degree and extent of damage done to the central nervous system, including the brain and sub-brain tissue which has to do with mentation and emotion.

When Duryea was committed to Matteawan in 1914, the prognosis seemed completely hopeless. He actually remained in a state of inertia and confusion for many years. He required frequent tube-feeding. His memory of his past was spotty and foggy. He was also under the delusion that it was a distant cousin named Chester Duryea (without the middle initial, "B") who had actually committed the crime. He claimed this despite the fact that the cousin was dead and had previously had no contact with the family for years.

At times he wrote bizarre letters signed either as "Dr. Duryea" or as "Major General God."

There was no question but that he was mentally disorganized for many years while at Matteawan.

The factor that marks this case as so remarkable, however, is that at the end of 18 years' residence in Matteawan (1932), Duryea began to regain his memory and his faculties of orientation. He started to write letters to attorneys seeking their advice. These were promptly referred by Matteawan authorities to the Counsel representing the Committee for his estate, which was a Brooklyn bank. When he finally sent a plea to the governor, the authorities decided that he was "getting worse."

It was not until 1940 that Duryea's release on a writ of habeas corpus was obtained by his lawyers, Mr. James D. C. Murray and Mr. Irving Greenberg. Between 1932 and 1940, the following (information supplied to me by Mr. Greenberg) took place:

Duryea could make no headway with the authorities at Matteawan regarding getting mail out to addressees.

The bank in Brooklyn, acting as Committee for Duryea's funds, was investing them in such manner as to cause substantial losses, with no accounting to anyone.

The wife, from whom Duryea had been legally separated even before the crime of 1914, was drawing $5,000 a year alimony, and their son, who had turned out to be a 'round-the-world drifter, was receiving $2,500 a year from the estate. Neither of these beneficiaries had ever visited the defendant.

Duryea finally succeeded in getting a letter out to Mr. Murray via a released Matteawan inmate, whose legal residence was in California. The latter referred it to his attorney in that state. That attorney called the letter to the attention of Mr. Murray. It was a letter appealing for legal assistance. This was in the year 1938. At that point, Mr. Murray and Mr. Greenberg visited Duryea in the hospital. After several lengthy interviews, the co-counsel concluded that, as of then, Duryea was competent to manage his own affairs without the assistance of a Committee; that he was capable of understanding the charges preferred against him in 1914 and of making a defense thereto.

In December 1939, a writ of habeas corpus authorizing the return of the defendant to await trial at the Raymond Street jail in Brooklyn, was sustained by the Honorable Mr. Justice Davis of the New York Supreme Court. It was appealed by the Attorney General in March 1940 on the grounds that the defendant was still insane and incompetent.

The minutes of that hearing are significant for an understanding of the degree of recovery achieved by the patient after 25 years of confinement.

The first witness called by Mr. Murray was the defendant, Chester B. Duryea.

Statistical data pertaining to birth, ancestry, education, marital status, etc., were reviewed in detail and the answers regarding these items were given with clarity as well as accuracy. Mr. Murray was obviously attempting to demonstrate the defendant's awareness of reality. This he did very convincingly in examining him regarding educational background and occupational adventures:

Q. *Did you go to school in New York City?* A. *I went to Columbia Grammar School in New York City.*

Q. *Where was the school?* A. *On 50th Street, between Madison and 4th Avenues.*

Q. *Then did you attend any other institutions of learning?* A. *Yes, the Columbia School of Mines—it was incorporated in Columbia University.*

Q. *Did you graduate from the School of Mines?* A. *No, I had an attack of typhoid fever and during my convalescence I joined the firm of Duryea & Co.*

Q. *What business pursuits were Duryea & Co. concerned or interested in?* A. *They began as manufacturers' agents.*

Q. *Of what product?* A. *Glucose, starch. We handled "Aunt Jemima" for a while and we handled "Maypole Soap."*

Q. *Now, from the time of your leaving the Columbia School of Mines up to 1914, did you do any research work in the chemistry of starches?* A. *Well, my first research began when the National Starch Co. attempted to stop "Duryea" from doing business with the Sioux City, Iowa, Starch Co. They used to send us under contract a couple of carloads of starch for examination—I developed a method to show that the product made by the Glen Cove Mfg. Co. was not the same as that product manufactured by Duryea Bros. I finally developed the Vicosometric Method which enabled me to show that.*

Later on in the hearing, the defendant, in response to questions, recounted that he had written several articles for publication at the request of Prof. Marsden Taylor Bogart, president of the American Chemical Society. The last one was printed in the Journal of Chemistry just prior to the defendant's commitment to Matteawan. A copy of this was shown to the Court.

The purpose of this latter interrogation was apparently to show that Mr. Duryea had recovered his memory.

Mr. Murray then elicited from the defendant the admission that he had been a periodic alcoholic since 1902 (12 years before the tragedy) and that he had been institutionalized several times because of his mental departures from reality.

About his ideas of claiming that he was "Major General God" and his practice of signing letters as Dr. Duryea, he readily admitted that they were partially imaginary. Logically, he maintained that though he had actually received no formal degree, he had demonstrated more scientific acumen than the majority of doctors he had seen "and particularly those at Matteawan."

He maintained that his pose as "Major General God" was a jest. His explanation was that most of the patients referred sneeringly to Dr. Keib, the Superintendent of Matteawan, as God, and that he, Duryea, having a long line of generals in his ancestral background, adopted with deliberation the fraudulent appellation.

He freely admitted that his idea of having been falsely identified with a cousin by the same name (minus the middle initial "B"), was a delusion.

The psychiatrists retained by the Committee seemed to be "playing it safe." They admitted marked improvement in Duryea's perceptions, but feared a relapse into homicidal urges upon the basis of delusion or misinterpretation. Yet, neither Dr. Gregory nor Dr. Cheney, both highly regarded and reputable, could pinpoint a single symptom at the time of their brief examination in 1939, that would label Duryea a psychotic person and incapable of understanding the charges pending against him. And the doctors at Matteawan could give no more information. Their notations were sketchy. Little or nothing could be gleaned from the record to indicate that Duryea had ever been examined thoroughly subsequent to his admission in 1914. The defendant himself admitted to years of mental confusion. Yet when he felt he was coming "out of the cloud," there was no help available. The Superintendent was obliged to refer all complaints to the Committee, which was the bank. Apparently he never took the trouble to investigate the validity of the complaints. The main pertinent notations on the record were made only after Mr. Murray had made his move in 1938 to have his client freed and prepared to stand trial. The psychiatrists retained by Mr. Murray, Drs. Cusack and Epstein, found Mr. Duryea to be in complete remission from the psychotic process. They testified to this. They also testified that while he had undergone a prolonged catatonic state, they were not certain as to its derivation.

Drs. Gregory and Cheney made the diagnosis of schizophrenia, unequivocally. Though Duryea had manifested some of the delusional ideation which was pathognomonic of the paranoid type of that disorder, the picture seems to me far from typical. In the first place, it is extremely unusual for the onset of this entity to occur as late as the forties. The beginnings in the vast majority of the cases become noticeable in adolescence or, at the latest, in the early thirties. In the second place, this case is one of the first I have heard of that persisted for 25 years without signs of deterioration, both intellectually and emotionally. I am more inclined to lay emphasis upon the influence of the alcoholic factors, i.e., the presence of the Korsakoff Syndrome, the symptoms of which I have described previously. The brain irritation in this disease may be evident temporarily, semi-permanently, or permanently. In this instance, the condition was evidently semi-permanent. From his testimony on the stand, it was obvious that Duryea had recovered his mental and emotional equilibrium. He also began to realize the imaginary implications of his former delusions.

Excerpts from the "Opinion of the Court" at the end of the hearing on the writ follow:

The relator (defendant), being confined to Matteawan State Hospital, is before this Court on a writ of habeas corpus. On May 5, 1914, he shot and killed his father. On June 5, 1914, he was committed to the present institution after an inquiry as to his sanity.—He has since been so confined.—The responsibility resting upon this Court is not to determine the mental condition of the relator at the time of the alleged act. That is for the jury.—The question before the Court is single: Has the relator so far recovered at this time from a state of insanity so as to be capable of understanding the proceedings and making a defense.

The Court then quoted the testimony of Dr. Cheney who, though he still expressed the opinion that Duryea was not fully recovered and required further institutional observation and care, stated: "His present mental condition is such that he can properly be brought to trial upon the pending indictment."

The Court stated further:

Dr. Wilner, regularly attached to Matteawan, and under whose direct supervision the relator (Mr. Duryea) has been for the last few years, expressed a similar opinion on cross-examination.

Dr. Gregory, a well-known authority of many years' standing, concluded his testimony—by the statement that he would not say "yes" nor would he say "no."

With the foregoing in mind, we turn to the testimony of the vital witness, the relator. Called by his counsel, he was upon the witness stand for several continuous days of the hearing and during that period of time he was cross-examined at length. His attitude was quiet, courteous and polite. Some portions of his testimony might be the object of criticism but on the whole his answers were intelligent, direct and responsive. The Court carefully observed him for days while he sat at the counsel table listening to the testimony of the experts. He was most attentive and normal in his reactions. At the conclusion of the entire hearing, after counsel for both parties had rested, the Court, without previous warning, recalled the witness to the stand. It was an unexpected and severe test. His responses to direct, and at times harsh questions by the Court were, in turn, direct and intelligent, demonstrating a clear understanding of the proceedings.

I am constrained to follow the opinion of the majority of the doctors plus my own observations, and therefore, grant the writ and order the relator returned to the proper authorities for trial upon the indictment.

The indictment was dismissed by Kings County Judge Martin, and the accused regained control of his monies and properties. Thereafter for 8 years before his death, he functioned normally. He cut off his profligate son and reduced the $5,000 annual alimony for his disinterested wife to $2500. That left him a yearly income of approximately $10,000. In his remaining years he lived a normal social life and did constructive work in photography. At no time did he show any signs of his previous mental disturbance. He kept in constant contact with Mr. Murray and his associate, Mr. Greenberg.

In this case, it is obvious that the prisoner achieved, during his period of incarceration, a recovery which was unquestionably productive and which warranted his release and return to society. His history after release justified the opinions of both the psychiatrists and the Court. There are aspects of the case which warrant further observation and study since the mechanisms involved in the actual remission of the psychosis are not understood in their entirety.

5

Two "charming" boy killers

Nathan Leopold, thrill killer of 1924, stepped through the Stateville Prison gate to freedom today after 33 years, 6 months and 2 days in prison.

NEW YORK POST, 3/13/58

IN THE three previous cases reported in this historical survey—the cases of Guiteau, Thaw, and Duryea—sufficient evidence was presented to convince even a layman that something was radically wrong with the mentality of the criminals. This does not hold true in the notorious Loeb-Leopold case. The accused were apparently bi-products of a peculiar twist in our ever-changing culture. At that time (1924), the "sky was the limit." Gangsters were running the show in Chicago. Morals in adolescent circles were at an infamous low. The line between recklessness and crime seemed to be somewhat blurred and, in the public mind, the law-breaker was often the hero.

Cold-bloodedly and with calculated deliberation, the two adolescents, Richard Loeb and Nathan Leopold, murdered the fourteen-year-old Bobby Franks. They used a chisel to inflict the lethal brain damages. After the act, they placed the body in an abandoned culvert with the intention of leading the authorities to believe that it was a drowning. A pair of dropped eyeglasses supplied the clue which later brought forth a full confession from the suspects.

The parents of both culprits retained psychiatrists to

demonstrate that the defendants were not responsible for the murder. Appearing for the defense were Drs. White, Bowman, Healty, and Glueck. Mr. Robert E. Crowe was the prosecutor. The state retained as psychiatrists Drs. Church, Patrick, Singer, and Krohn. The fees of all the psychiatrists were the same, $250 a day, the fixed emolument allowed by the State of Illinois. There was no suspicion of connivance such as many feared had existed in the Thaw case.

The Loeb-Leopold case raged around a clash of ideologies. The prosecutors and psychiatrists for the state stressed the necessity for punitive measures. The defense, that is Dr. William A. White, and Defense Counsel, Clarence Darrow, urged the need for leniency because of the emotional immaturity of the adolescent offenders.

As far as I can discern from the reports of the case, Loeb was the instigator. The psychiatrists and attorneys for the defense brought out the fact—one not denied by the prosecution—that he (Loeb), prior to the Franks affair, had planned the kidnapping of a young girl. He had even entertained the idea of absconding with his younger brother. To Dr. White and the other psychiatrists for the defense, he described fantasies of being a central figure in banditry and hold-ups. Even while in jail, he exulted in being a "famous criminal." He looked upon killing as "a necessary part of any crime."

Leopold seems to have become involved for two reasons: One, he thought he was capable of master-minding and carrying through the "perfect murder," something he was eager to do for the sake of his already inflated ego;

and, two, he wished to be the "behind-the-scenes hero" in the eyes of Loeb, for whom he admittedly cherished abnormal sensual desires.

Bobby Franks, the victim, was chosen practically at random. Both defendants were wealthy. They had no need for extra money. They committed the heinous crime for "a thrill," under the obviously dramatic pretext of wanting a ransom.

This was, I say again, a peculiar period in our history—a time of speakeasies, of devil-may-care attitudes, of lawbreakers who were not only accepted but even lionized. Al Capone gave lavish parties at his fabulous home in Florida. Pious churchgoers were known to accept invitations to them. Random killings were rife. It is conceivable that two adolescents, in the spirit of this age, may have contrived the slaying of Bobby Franks with careless gaiety.

Dr. White and Mr. Darrow did their best to save the criminals. I was, at the time, a psychiatric interne at Saint Elizabeth's Hospital in Washington, D.C. Dr. White was our chief. I recall clearly the statements made by Dr. White when he returned from the trial in Chicago. "The boys were perfectly charming," he told the staff. He quoted Leopold as remarking, "I am so glad to meet you, Dr. White. I know the exact number of lines you take up in *Who's Who*." He described the "King-Slave" fantasy on the part of Leopold as though it might constitute an extenuating circumstance in his guilt. Leopold was the slave, doing the bidding of the "king," Loeb, to assist him in master-minding the "perfect crime."

Mr. Darrow's summation was a dramatic one. He leaned heavily upon emotional reactions rather than on cold, indisputable facts. For example, he called attention to "our anxiety over this case . . . being due to the almost unheard-of publicity . . . the verdict may be the result of prejudice alone." This, indeed, must have been an affront to the Court. Yet, if it was, it was not noticeable. He pleaded further, "If poor little Bobby Franks could be brought back to life by the hanging of these two boys, I'd say, 'let them go'." He then quoted from the poet, Housman:

"Now hollow fires burn out to black and lights are fluttering low,
Square your shoulders, lift your pack and leave your friends and go.
Oh, never fear, lads, naught's to dread,
Look nor to left or right; in all the endless road you tread.
There's nothing but the night."

The quotation was evidently used to refer to the impending death sentence or to the alternative of life imprisonment. Mr. Darrow also quoted Omar Khayyam:

"So I be written in the Book of Love,
I do not care about the Book above.
Erase my name, or write it as you will,
So I be written in the Book of Love."

All of this was very effective. The pertinent point of responsibility regarding the murder still remained, however. Loeb and Leopold had planned and executed a premeditated crime. Had it occurred yesterday, in the light of the current wave of juvenile wanton killings, I am quite certain that a jury would have found them guilty of murder in the first degree. A line must be drawn somewhere. Or no person will be considered responsible for any act of violence!

The prosecutor, Mr. Crowe, expostulated to the Court, as follows:

All I want to say, your Honor . . . that if a jury were sitting in that box and returned a verdict without death punishment, every person in the community, including your Honor, as well as myself, would feel that the verdict was founded upon corruption.

He underlined his point by emphasizing the fact that both defendants were disciples of the Nietzschean philosophy which purportedly advocated "freedom from scruple and (being) above legal entanglements."

I am inclined to discount the contention that the murder was connected with the writings of the philosopher. If it was, then it happened only through misinterpretation. In none of his works, did Nietzsche advocate or condone physical violence. He underscored the importance of freedom from intellectual bondage.

Dr. White and Mr. Darrow saved Loeb and Leopold from the death sentence. They may have been aided by the coincidence that a movement, promulgated by the National Committee for Mental Hygiene, was on foot at the time (1925) to exonerate youthful criminal activities on the grounds of hopes for rehabilitation. Loeb and Leopold were regarded as mentally aberrant. Yet, never during the trial was evidence brought forth to prove that either was mentally ill. And neither culprit, during the entire period of imprisonment, manifested any signs of insanity.

The defendants were sentenced to prolonged incarceration. Loeb was murdered in prison a few years ago in the course of a homosexual debauch. Leopold was, at all times, a model prisoner, behaving perfectly and helping in the instruction of other prisoners. Numerous appeals were made for his release. The fear that a dangerous precedent might be set if he were freed served to negate most of these appeals.

But on March 13, 1958, Nathan Leopold walked out of prison to begin life again as a laboratory worker in a Puerto Rican Hospital. His statement to the press just before his release was: "Thousands of prisoners, especially long-term prisoners, look to me to vindicate the rehabilitation theory of imprisonment. I will do my best not to fail that trust."

The outcome of this historic case has stirred great public interest. From a psychiatric point of view, however, it offers very little. No criteria of worthwhile significance have emerged. To begin with, Leopold was never a psychotic. And the factors which permitted him to develop into "a socially conscious and responsible person" did not operate similarly in the case of his partner in crime who died in violence. According to our present interpretation of law and psychiatry, both Loeb and Leopold should have suffered the full penalty for their crime and Leopold, even 33 years later, should not have been released. But the readmission of any person previously lost to the society of man is meaningful. If Leopold justifies the faith that has been bestowed upon him, it will indeed be a fortunate achievement.

6 The other self takes over

As the court clerk intoned, "Bayard P. Peakes, you have been indicted for first degree murder . . ." Peakes looked about the courtroom as if he thought the charge was meant for another.

NEW YORK TIMES, 7/20/52

NONE OF US is certain about the exact nature of the mental disorder called schizophrenia. Kraepelin, the father of our modern psychiatry, merely categorized the disease entity in a descriptive sense, though implying that it had an organic base. Bleuler, on the other hand, seemed to believe that there were environmental elements conditioning its metamorphosis. Freud contended that it was the extension of a psychoneurotic process but he admitted the possibility of organicity. My colleague, Dr. Lauretta Bender, has always insisted that schizophrenia was primarily organic, an abnormality connected with the inner workings of the brain and having little to do with environment. She has given vivid descriptions of schizophrenic manifestations in children. She is unquestionably a pioneer in this field of childhood schizophrenia.

Dr. Francis Dercum, a number of years ago, wrote a book describing his convictions that even the psychoneurotic reactions had an organic base, in that reservoir of emotivity, the thalamus (a sub-brain department governing the emotions exclusively, not the reasoning capacity). He mentioned instances wherein the neurotic symptoms (anxiety, compulsion, obsession, phobias, etc.) had become manifest in infancy.

The research work of Dr. Heath at Tulane University has demonstrated conclusively that there is a significant contrast in the histology of the blood cells in known schizophrenics and those showing no symptoms of that disorder. Dr. Heath actually produced schizophrenic-like symptoms in a group of ostensibly non-schizophrenic volunteers by injecting the blood of the former into the veins of the latter.

By way of illustration, I am reporting three examples of schizophrenics who committed murders. Two of them showed no overt symptoms (delusions, hallucinations, or distortions in emotivity) prior to adolescence. In the third case, the schizophrenic symptomatology became discernible in the formative years of childhood.

Here is the first:

Early one morning in the summer of 1953, a young man strode into the building at Columbia University which housed the Physics Department. His entrance was unchallenged. From his appearance—tall, pale, gaunt, with closely cropped hair, he could easily have been mistaken for a faculty member. Having ascended the stairway to the third floor he entered the first office in which the door was ajar. There, according to his account (there were no witnesses), he observed a young female stenographer assorting material as if in preparation for the day's work. He inquired as to the whereabouts of Professor X. Jestingly she replied that it was rather ridiculous for him to expect the Professor in at that hour (before 9 A.M.).

Thereupon the defendant drew a revolver from his pocket, firing it and killing her instantly. He then calmly made his exit and left for his native New England.

According to the police reports, he was picked up three days later in Boston by New York detectives. The police account contained the statement that "he admitted his guilt willingly, at length, and with no degree of remorse." Similarly, the District Attorney described him as "interested but not seemingly concerned about what was happening." The District Attorney stated further that the defendant admitted killing the deceased because "she was the only person he found in the American Physical Society office where he went to kill some physicists. . . . His reason for so doing was to obtain publicity that would win an audience for his electronic ideas." Reportedly, he had also entertained ideas of going to some newspaper offices and killing a few editors in the hope of gaining more publicity for his theories.

Following his arrest in Boston, Peakes made no effort to fight his extradition. In New York, he was immediately committed to Bellevue for mental observation.

At Bellevue, he was completely cooperative, readily volunteered the information that "I am the fellow who murdered the girl and they sent me here for N-P (neuropsychiatric) observation. I killed her to get attention to my thesis. If the papers would publish it (13,000 words), the electron theory would be disproven and I think that this would be a substitute for Christ."

Ordinarily, such a brash statement would be a significant factor in the diagnostic evaluation, pointing to mental aberration. In this instance, however, a number of other important considerations were also involved. Peakes had completed high school successfully in Maine. He was registered in Bates College in that state when the war broke out. He enlisted in the Canadian forces and served creditably for four years. In 1945, he was transferred to the Services in the U.S.A. Whether this was a result of mental disturbance or not is questionable. Nevertheless, in 1945, he received a 50% discharge from the Cushing General Hospital on a neuropsychiatric basis. According to the rigid interpretations of the Veterans' Administration, his mental status was regarded as psychoneurotic rather than psychotic.

His ideational stability was further borne out by his activities after his discharge. Under the G. I. Bill of Rights he had completed three of the four required years in pre-medical training at Northeastern University in Boston. He had been accepted as a member of the American Physical Society. He had gotten out of good standing but principally on the grounds that he had been opposed to Oppenheimer's theory of nuclear energy.

Five days after his admission to Bellevue, I conducted a face-to-face examination of Peakes. Excerpts of this interview, as well as later ones, follow:

Q. *How do you feel?* A. *All right.*

Q. *Where born?* A. *Maine.*

Q. *How many children in the family?* A. *I have a brother and a sister.*

Q. *As a result of being the youngest, were you like many, favored?* A. *No, I don't think there was any difference. My brother and I used to work on a farm together.*

Q. *What about school?* A. *In grade school I did pretty well, and in high school I was a normal student.*

Q. *Friends?* A. *No; well, I had one I used to study with in high school and then sort of broke away.*

Q. *Girls?* A. *I tried with one or two, but they didn't want to date me. I didn't dance or go to school dances.*

Q. *Did you do well in high school?* A. *I did pretty well in French, B plus; English I did good. Latin I did B; mathematics B; physics and chemistry I liked better and got B plus.*

Q. *Did you become especially interested in physics at that time?* A. *Yes, particularly in electronics.*

Q. *Then how did it happen that you pointed for medicine?* A. *I was possessed with the idea that it was possible for a man to do drug research that would make him live forever.*

Q. *About when did this theory occur to you?* A. *When I was 16. It was then that I got the idea that electrons were not only unnecessary, but did not exist.*

Q. *Then just what is your conception of the nature of electricity?* A. *Something superior to supersonic sound; more delicate, finer disturbances. Superior motivation or excitation within the conductor.*

Q. *Usually in a book the author comes to some conclusion. At what conclusion did you arrive from what you have told us?* A. *It is electric current within a wire, motion within a wire, the supercharge being a necessity of wave disturbance within a conductor.*

Q. *Describe electrons.* A. *So much air taken out—the reason you get a light is because you have less air. It is easily motivated like a current. You get so much glow. You have a beam which resembles iron because it is supposed to beat back and forth with the electromagnet, just as though playing with iron at either end. It is the ideal condition for pressure charge of electromagnet sound waving.*

Q. *I believe that you told us that you had a number of articles in pamphlet form printed at your own expense?* A. *Yes; eighty-six in the first series, several hundred in the second and six hundred in the third.*

Q. *What was the title, or titles of the series?* A. *Practical explanation of science! I sent copies to all the members of the American Physical Society, including the President. My ideas were either rejected or ignored. I felt that if I didn't make that murder, they wouldn't do anything.*

Q. *Did you ever attempt to meet Dr. Oppenheimer, whose theory of nuclear physics you sought to disprove?* A. *I talked to a scientist who won the Nobel Prize, who would be qualified in directing me.*

Q. *Suppose that you had met Dr. Oppenheimer that morning that you visited the Department of Physics at Columbia, what would you have done?* A. *I would have done the same thing that I did to the girl—kill him. My project was of more importance than the atomic bomb. I had the same idea about certain newspaper editors who refused to pay any attention to the letters I wrote them in regard to my theories.*

As a result of the examinations, a detailed report was submitted to the Court, delineating the psychiatric findings which indicated that the defendant was a suitable case for commitment to a state hospital for the mentally ill. The presence of psychotic thinking was unmistakable. Defendant's counsel made no objection to controvert the decision. Legal procedure requires, however, that an additional formal hearing be held. Here is a word picture of the hearing:

Pursuant to an order by the Honorable Saul S. Streit, Judge of the Court of General Sessions, directing that a formal hearing be held in the case of the above mentioned defendant in accordance with the provisions of the Code of Criminal Procedure, this formal hearing was held in the Psychiatric Division of Bellevue Hospital on (date withheld) *in the summer of 1952, by the two qualified psychiatrists signing the report* (Dr. Theodore S. Weiss, my associate, and myself.)

The following were present at this hearing: Dr. John H. Cassity, Senior Psychiatrist in charge of the Prison Service, Bellevue Psychiatric Hospital, Dr. Theodore S. Weiss, Psychiatrist in charge of the male prison ward, Dr. Petty L. Lichtenstein, Medical Advisor to the District

Attorney's office, Mr. Vincent Dermody, Assistant District Attorney attached to the Homicide Branch, Mr. Anthony Alfano, Assistant Corporation Counsel, and Mr. James D. C. Murray, attorney for the defendant.

The following witnesses, who were subpoenaed, testified under oath: Detective J— the arresting officer, Mr. F— Assistant Chief Attorney, Regional Office of the Veterans' Administration; Mr. —, uncle of the defendant, of Boston, Mass.

The arresting officer recounted the relatively effortless and uncomplicated way in which he had traced and arrested the defendant in Boston, added that he was amazed at his attitude of abandonment and indifference in making a full confession of his guilt and offering no resistance to extradition proceedings. He seemed to feel glad that it happened.

The testimony given by the representative from the Veterans' Administration was extremely vague and uninformative. The reason for this was learned later. The family of the deceased had instituted legal proceedings against the government on the grounds that the defendant had been released prematurely and unwarrantedly from a veterans' facility.

Neither Mr. Murray, chief counsel for the defendant, nor Dr. Lichtenstein, the psychiatrist from the District Attorney's office, registered any objections to our findings (Dr. Weiss's and mine).

The defendant's uncle from Boston, made the following statement:

When 18, he got through high school and had done well. I urged that he go to college. I was told that he was accepted. Three or four weeks before the beginning of the term, I had a letter from the college, asking me if he was going because they had notified him and had heard nothing. He wrote me that he didn't believe he was going to college in the light of what was taking place, i. e., World War II. He then enlisted in the Canadian Army. I did not see him again until 1945. Subsequent to his enlistment, he had been transferred to the American Forces. In the year mentioned, the Red Cross telephoned me from New York that he was in Cushing General Hospital. I saw him during that summer every week. He was completely mentally gone when I saw him. He visited my home several times from 1946 to 1949. He would talk about freezing bodies and keeping them for 500 years. I tried as best I could to urge him not to continue school. I knew that he wasn't competent to do things. He talked a good deal of electronics; that everyone was wrong and that he had the truth about electricity and that the others operating under the theory of electronics did not.

The defendant was then brought in for examination. Excerpts of our report regarding his deportment and behavior at the time, follow:

During the hearing the defendant was relaxed to the point of being casual. His discussion of the crime was uttered in a rather monotonous, stereotyped tone of voice and he frequently smiled in an inane manner when describing the tragedy. When questioned regarding his theory which would eliminate the presence of electrons, he became incoherent and referred us to his brochure, stating "It is all in the last chapter and paragraph" (of a 30-page paper captioned "Practical explanation of science"). The last paragraph, which he advised us to consult, read as follows: "In conclusion I would like to say that I hope the reader has not gone through this thesis with a complete faith in the electronic theory. I think that in a careful, thorough consideration of all points on both sides, the reader will come to the same conclusion that I have. Here is the general definition of the electric current as I find it to be: the electric current is a supersonic motivation in a conductor which is of necessity a wave disturbance; and it is created and persists only where there is a contrast, or potential difference between two points and its line of propagation."

He stated further that he had required Dr. Oppenheimer, the nuclear physicist, to recommend him for the Nobel Prize as a reward for his above mentioned "innovation." He reiterated his original intention of "dispatching" some of the assistant physicists at Harvard and also some newspaper editors who had refused to give publicity to his ideas. As to the murder itself, he stated that he had no regrets. He said: "It's just like a soldier doing his duty for the benefit of mankind." He laughed frequently in a silly and inappropriate manner throughout the proceedings.

Taking the above mentioned statements and reactions

into consideration, it is evident to the examiners that this defendant is, and has been for many years, the victim of a schizophrenic process of the paranoid (persecutory) type and is a suitable case for commitment to Matteawan State Hospital for the Criminally Insane, at Beacon, New York.

7

Religio-racial hallucinations

A 64-year-old maniac, impelled by a twisted religious complex, fired wildly into a group of high school boys yesterday afternoon, killing one and wounding six others.

HERALD-TRIBUNE, 3/16/48

THE SECOND DEFENDANT in our schizophrenia series had been afflicted with the disorder for over 20 years and, for approximately that length of time, had nurtured the delusion that he was followed and thwarted in his pursuits by Catholics, especially by those of Italian descent. The obsession seems to have stemmed from actual animosities flaring up in his early adulthood between the Italians and the Yugoslavs. Marko L. Markovich, the defendant, was born and reared in Yugoslavia. The onset of his psychosis, however, occurred several years after his immigration to this country. Twice, while employed as a laborer in Arizona, he was committed to a mental institution in that state. The report received from the state hospital in Phoenix was not very informative, though it did indicate that his commitments had resulted from "acts of violence: 1) an attempt to kill an inmate whom he had never seen before, and 2) an unprovoked assault upon a blood cousin." During one of his periods of commitment, he laid claim to being an emperor. To us at Bellevue, he denied recollection of these events. The letter from the Arizona institution failed to mention either the diagnosis or the circumstances surrounding his release. But he was at large in the community for several years despite the evident fact that he was dangerously psychotic.

An event transpiring in 1944 seemingly triggered an acute exacerbation of the smoldering schizophrenic process. His 13-year-old son died, apparently from natural causes. The defendant, however, tied the tragic event in with his delusional system. He became convinced that death had resulted from a plot between his estranged wife and the Catholics.

And now for the murder itself:

In the Spring of 1948, a group of students were emerging from the yard of a Catholic school on their way to an armory around the corner. According to Detective Dunn, attached to the District Attorney's office, the defendant suddenly appeared outside the school, brandishing two guns. He fired several shots at random into the crowd of children, killing one boy and wounding six others. When he was arrested, he gave as his reason his conviction that he had been hounded by Italians and Catholics and that the latter had been responsible in 1944 for the death of his son.

The day following his arrest, Markovich was committed by the Court to Bellevue for mental observation. Both at the time of his admission and thereafter throughout his three weeks' stay, his behavior on the ward was exemplary. It was only when discussing his fancied persecutory injustices that he displayed marked agitation and truculence.

His own story follows:

In 1944, my wife told me my son die. She say that he was in good health in the morning and that night she find him dead with green stuff on his lips. I figure he go in the street and the Black Hand grab him and choke him. They are against Yugoslavs. They want to kill all of them. It must have been church propaganda. The doctor say my boy had hemorrhage of the head. Why he no look inside the body? (He seemed to infer that the Church and the doctor were in collusion.) *I decide to kill the men who kill my boy. I buy gun in Reno in 1944 and one in California in 1945. I decide to get the killers slowly. I come to New York. All of the restaurants are against me. I go from cafeteria to lunch-room. Then I try to find out what school my boy went to. Then I look around the old neighborhood, and I see this school—Catholic school. He played with those kids. Might be for some propaganda they kill him. I am out to kill the devil who kill my son. Last April I come here. I go to 62nd Street where he used to live. I see Paulist church. I look around for school near that church. My boy used to play at that school at 61st Street and they didn't want him to beat them. Last Friday I go to 61st Street and see kids in yard. I find that it is a Catholic school. Monday I get a gun, try to open school door, but can't get in. Then I go to Central Park and at 3 o'clock I go back. The kids come out and I follow. I see them going to the Armory and I start shooting—for my son. I shot them to open the case and find out who was guilty of killing my son. I did it to get action by bringing the thing to public attention. I thought if I didn't kill some of them* (*Catholics, Italian Blackhand and political propagandists*), *they would kill me. I know they kill someone nearly every day. Twice before, they try to kill me on Good Friday.* (His son died on Palm Sunday and the instant offense was committed on a Monday preceding Good Friday.)

The remarkable feature in this case was that during the four years that he had been carrying guns for the purpose of avenging his son's demise, Markovich had outwardly manifested no violent tendencies. He was certainly seething inwardly with hatred towards Catholics. He was sure that they had contrived and perpetrated the murder of his child. His resolve was fierce and unrelenting, however. When he finally projected his delusional ideas, it was upon innocent children. They, as Catholics and former playmates of his son, were, in his distorted mind, the parties to his boy's death.

Both Peakes and Markovich are classical cases of the paranoid type of schizophrenia. Each murdered as the result of inflexible delusional ideation which rendered him powerless to resist a criminal act that he felt, and continued to feel, was fully justified. This variety of schizophrenia is the usual one encountered in schizophrenic criminals.

The other types of schizophrenics rarely resort to an act of crime. The hebephrenic type, so named because he is in a chronic state of hebetude or passivity, is completely lacking in acute sensitivity. He lives in a world of fantasy where he is preoccupied with relatively meaningless auditory and visual hallucinations. The catatonic type shuts himself off completely from reality. He either withdraws into a stupor or flies into a maniacal state which has no perceptible connection with his immediate environment. The simple type shows a marked blunting which restricts his ability to relate emotionally to other people.

Markovich was committed for life to the Matteawan State Hospital for the Criminally Insane.

8 Portent of crime in childhood

A trail along which police said they questioned at least 100 women, picking up a clue here, another there and finally piecing them all together, led Monday to the arrest of an ex-convict charged with a Chinatown hold-up murder on August 5.

JOURNAL-AMERICAN, 10/19/54

THE THIRD CASE in this series is an example of childhood schizophrenia. The validity of such a diagnosis, incidentally, is questioned in some psychiatric circles.

But I am in accord with Dr. Bender in her conviction that schizophrenia is an organic and therefore a fundamental process, rather than a functional one resulting from environmental conditioning. It is the problem of the psychiatrist to detect the presence of the disorder in its incipiency, that is, in the formative years of life. The principal obstacle in the diagnosis is the difficulty of obtaining accurate historical background. Relatives are usually unable to recall incidents which have meaning for the physician in his later examination. Like many of my colleagues, I fall occasionally into the practice of loosely labelling all individuals with immoral or anti-social tendencies as sociopaths. Time and again, Dr. Benjamin Karpman, of St. Elizabeth's Hospital at various psychiatric meetings and conventions, has emphasized that this procedure is not only untenable, but fallacious. He stresses the fact that most of the people whom we describe as sociopaths are fundamentally psychoneurotics, cyclothymics (persons subject to alternating waves of depression and elation) and, most frequently, schizophrenics.

In the case that follows, it was the pertinent information, supplied by relatives, dating back to the defendant's early childhood, that enabled me to make a more accurate diagnosis.

Radames Freyre, a 29-year-old Puerto Rican, arrived in the United States in 1945. By 1947, he was jailed on an assault charge and sent to the penal institution at Woodbourne. Later, he was transferred to Dannemora, which houses prisoners who have developed mental illnesses while in confinement. He was released from jail in 1952. After that, he worked at odd jobs in restaurants.

On the police blotter, a crime of murder was recorded as of August 1954. How Fu Lien, age 30, had been fatally shot in his home during the commission of a stick-up. His room-mate, Ching Vun Gee, had been pistol-whipped by Freyre and his accomplice. The attackers had fled, without taking the $400 that was in the apartment, when Lien, mortally wounded, crawled to the door, opened it, and shouted for help. Gee identified Freyre as the killer. Neighbors, shoppers, and clerks in the downstairs stores supplied further information.

Freyre was found sleeping in an auto in Harlem and taken into custody in October 1954. At that time, he made, both to the arresting officer and to the District Attorney, categorical denials of any knowledge of the crime.

But the police supplied items of information that were unmistakable. So did the dead man's room-mate. Freyre was convicted by a jury on a charge of murder in the first degree.

During the trial, denial was his sole defense. He berated his counsel for having advised him to accept a lesser plea. He accused the lawyer of collusion with the District Attorney.

The attitude of the defendant was noted by the judge who also took into consideration, apparently, his flat refusal to accept a plea of murder in the second degree which would have spared him electrocution. The court ordered a psychiatric evaluation.

In psychiatric contacts, Freyre revealed himself as seclusive and retarded. He responded to all questions hesitatingly. He was, at all times, suspicious and mistrustful.

As early as the age of 9, he admitted, he had the impression that he was being trailed by "dead people." He had complained then that "people were always bothering me." When asked in what respect, he said, "They try to influence my mind." When asked if that sort of thing was going on here, too, he replied, "That is right."

He went on to state his belief in being able to read other peoples' minds. He complained to the nurses that his food and cigarettes were being poisoned. At one time, he expressed the idea that his attorney, Mr. Suarez, had "planted a fellow" in the ward to watch him. He held steadfastly to his claim that he had not been convicted and continued to repeat, "I was just charged by the jury." When asked his preference regarding Matteawan versus death, he answered, "To die is better." He asked to "go free" as though nothing had happened.

My diagnostic impression at this point was quite definitely that of childhood schizophrenia. I went next to interview the mother. Her statement follows:

When he was 6 or 7, often, instead of going to school, he'd go to the river. He wouldn't come home for lunch or supper. He didn't want to sleep in the house. He used to go under the house. Sometimes he went downstairs looking for people he said wanted to kill him. (Friends?) *Not many. He had a dog and used to sleep with him under the house and I'd go out looking for him. He was always upset. Imagined people were against him. I think this was imaginary. While in the U. S. he still talked the same way. Here, he says there's a war going on outside the hospital.* (What did he say about the crime?) *He said Mr. Suarez is not his lawyer; that he is a District Attorney and that what happened to him wasn't a trial. He said the lawyer Suarez charged the jury.* (Why not take him to a doctor in childhood?) *We tried to persuade him to go but he wouldn't. He told me he wanted to kill himself.* (Before the crime?) *Yes, and even before he went to prison the first time. He always told me that.*

A sister who was present at the interview corroborated the statements of the mother and, in addition, reported that he fought with his brothers for no reason and never seemed to care what happened to him or to anyone else.

He just wasn't interested in anything. Here, he told me Suarez is persecuting him and that it wasn't a trial. He said, "there's a hypnotist here in Bellevue that tells me things." He warned me not to talk to anybody. He said there was a war outside . . . and to go and take care of mother. Then he left me. I called him back, but he wouldn't come.

The statements of the mother and sister served conclusively to substantiate my original impression. The patient is still in Matteawan. Had his condition been merely a reactive psychotic state, he would undoubtedly have recovered long before the end of his three-year residence at that institution. In my opinion, this is certainly a case where childhood schizophrenia served as the underlying cause of the crime of murder.

9

An impulse assumes command

A week-long police manhunt for the slaying of Mrs. Frieda Frank ended today when a flashily dressed man admitted the fatal mugging of the 49-year-old refugee, who was found dying last Wednesday near the door of her Washington Heights apartment, the police reported. The suspect, Theodore Samuels, 20, Negro, was booked on a charge of homicide.

SUN, 6/9/48

THOSE OF Theodore Samuels' assault victims who escaped death called him "The Apeman." His appearance was decidedly Simian. And his approach to his crime was unfailingly the same. Stealthily, he would stalk his prey—invariably female—stun her with a blow in the throat similar to that used in the Judo tactics he had learned in the Army, and then snatch her pocketbook. There had been thirteen of these assaults, none fatal, however. But in the last case, he followed the Judo assault with deliberate strangulation. In his own words, "I saw her walk along Broadway near 155 Street and I saw her enter the apartment house. As she put the key into the door, I asked her directions to Fort Washington Avenue. As she turned and pointed, I gave her a Commando assault. I hit her in the windpipe with the edge of the palm of my right hand and she fell to the floor. I fell on top of her, for I had lost my balance."

Apparently, it was when he fell that he decided to add the item of strangulation to his usual procedure. There were no witnesses.

It was Samuels' own father who came to the Police to report his son. The boy's behavior had been even stranger than usual. And newspaper descriptions led the father to his sad and accurate suspicions.

Theodore made no resistance when the police apprehended him in the home of his parents. On the contrary, he readily admitted having committed not only this murder, but the thirteen previous assaults and robberies, as well. He voluntarily produced Mrs. Frank's pocketbook and those of the other victims.

His very crassness seemed to me indicative of distorted thought processes. A study of the family background revealed no influences which would necessarily have led to murderous tendencies. His Army record disclosed that he had been charged with murder while in Service. But the circumstances had been extenuating and he had been absolved.

During his period of observation at Bellevue, he was at all times well-behaved, affable, even genial. He consorted freely with those about him and made good contact with the examiners—two facts used later with telling effect by the prosecution. As the observation progressed, however, it became more and more evident that Theodore Samuels was totally bereft of normal emotionality. Grossly disordered thinking resulted. For example, he was asked, "Are you worried about being charged with first degree murder?"

He replied:

My own philosophy of life—it has been said that he is not fit to live so he must die. Dying is as material as living. They call it death. That fear of death is what holds the great masses under control. Fear of death keeps them on the straights. To be afraid, I'd be torturing myself on earth. A person can put aside fear over a period of time when a person or people want to know the truth and all that sort of stuff. You can reach each point where everything is passing—changing into something else after a period of time. Why did I latch onto anything that happens

Q. *But murder is a capital crime!* A. *Killing is a material thing. I do not separate man from animal. Man turns to his original state of mind.*

Q. *What about concern for your victim?* A. *Oh, she was perhaps 40 years old. Perhaps our world lines crossed.*

Q. *What lines?* A. *I figured it out that they are fixed from birth.*

Q. *What about your numerous attacks on other women?* A. *They couldn't be avoided. Just like two automobiles hit each other. They cease them to exist in this form of life.*

The thinking was indeed bizarre and unrealistic! We requested a formal hearing. Dr. Morris Herman and I, as Commissioners, examined the defendant in the presence of (1) the Assistant District Attorney and the psychiatrist attached to the office of the District Attorney. (2) Counsel for the defense and any medical witnesses which he might have seen fit to summon. (3) A representative of the office of the Corporation Counsel. Additional witnesses included the arresting officer and relatives of the defendant.

Excerpts from the minutes of the initial hearing follow: Witness; Arresting Officer.

Questioning by Dr. Cassity: Q. *We would like to know some of the outstanding circumstances connected with the arrest of this defendant. Could you tell us something about your observations of him at the time of the arrest?* A. *At about 8:30 on June the 8th, while patrolling Post 33 which runs from 156 to 159th on Broadway, a man approached me and asked me if I could come to his house. He said that his son was acting peculiarly and that he was cutting up pictures in the house. . . . Upon entering the apartment I heard the radio playing so loudly you couldn't hear yourself think or talk. I saw a young fellow standing in the room next to the window, with a brown pork pie hat on, brown sports jacket, blue pants and brown shoes and a pipe in his mouth. I asked him his name and how old he was and he answered both questions correctly. He started telling me about a piano that had been taken away from him.* (Apparently attributable to his noise-making in the early morning hours.) *His father told me that he kept repeating, "Someone will die tonight. . . ." I saw a lady and her daughter at the bottom of the steps. I asked them who they were and they said that they were the boy's mother and sister and they told me the same thing about somebody having to die. Then I asked him about the knife which he had used in cutting up the pictures, he said that he kept it for protection. . . . I then wanted to know if he had been in the Service. He said he had served four months in the Navy and that he couldn't stand it and he got out on an undesirable discharge. Then he entered the Army and spent three and a half years overseas.* (It was during this tenure of service that he was charged with, but exonerated of manslaughter.)

Questioning by Dr. Herman, my associate examiner: Q. *Did you ask him why he was playing the radio so loudly?* A. *He said that he liked music. When I entered the room it was almost vibrating with the tone.*

Q. *Was it loud enough to be heard in the adjoining buildings?* A. *I think so.*

Q. *When you came in, what was his reaction?* A. *As I seen him when I came in, he was standing by the window and he had his pipe in his mouth and he was twitching his eyes and lips and puffing on his pipe. . . .*

Q. *Did he say why he was cutting up pictures?* A. *He just said that he had the urge.*

Q. *You arrested him and also saw him arraigned in court. What was his reaction on these occasions?* A. *He stood still and answered all questions normally.*

Questioning by Dr. Lichtenstein, psychiatrist attached to the District Attorney's Office: Q. *Were you present at the District Attorney's office when I questioned him?* A. *Yes, sir.*

Q. *At that time did he impress you as being a person a little bit out of his mind?* A. *I don't believe so.*

Q. *Do you remember him saying why he kept the*

pocketbook? A. *I know that he said that he kept the pocketbook for the beauty of it.*

Questioning by Mr. Mendelson: Q. *I asked him what kind of jobs he was doing and he told me he had been working in a record shop. He also referred to other odd jobs on 160th and 161st Streets and Riverside Drive. There are no businesses there?* A. *No, just a residential section.*

Q. *Why did he say he collected the pocketbooks?* A. *He said that he kept them "for the beauty of it all."*

Prosecution was striving to obtain a conviction of deliberate, first degree murder, preconceived and premeditated.

The psychiatric contention that the defendant was mentally ill both before and at the time of the offense of which he was accused.

The prosecutor insisted that he was not only guilty but a malingerer.

And the testimony went on.

Witness; Miriam E., sister of the defendant.

Statement by Dr. Cassity: *This is a hearing before a Commission to attempt to evaluate the mental status of your brother.*

Questioning by Dr. Herman: Q. *You are a nurse?* A. *Yes, I am at Harlem Hospital.*

Q. *Where were you employed previously?* A. *At the Brooklyn Jewish Hospital.*

Q. *Were you ever a nurse in connection with psychiatric cases?* A. *I had an affiliation with psychiatry which was a part of my 5-year course, 4 months at a Veterans Hospital, Tuskegee, Alabama.*

Q. *Tell us briefly something about the early life and habits of your brother.* A. *Well, Theodore always liked being alone. Even when he was quite young, 10 or 12, he was always alone by himself and you wouldn't know where he was. . . . Before finishing high school he became restless and went to work on a dairy farm out West. Even then he seemed to be very peculiar.*

Q. *Why do you say that he was peculiar?* A. *He didn't want to talk to people. He seemed to have a complex that he was being persecuted and was inferior.*

Questioning by Dr. Cassity: Q. *In what respect did he appear inferior?* A. *He wouldn't come in the living room. If we had company he would go to his room and would come out when they left.*

Q. *Why?* A. *He says I can't cope with society. I'm a criminal. I'm no good. I'm inferior to you. Twice he drank iodine. He showed us the bottles and the vomitus was on the spread.*

Q. *Why did he say he took it?* A. *He said he wanted to die. . . .*

Q. *Did he go to a doctor?* A. *No, he asked us to carry him.*

Q. *What kind of a doctor?* A. *To Bellevue. We laughed at him. He said "I'm not kidding. . . ."*

Q. *You were a nurse at that time. You had also had some psychiatric contacts at the time. Why didn't you take it more seriously when he asked to come here?* A. *I'll be frank. We did not want to institutionalize him because we loved him and wanted to keep him with us. We did not laugh a little later when he began to act very queer.*

Q. *When was that?* A. *The latter part of February.* (3 months prior to the murder.)

Q. *How queer?* A. *He took a turkey shaped glass dish and crushed it. I remember having shown my mother something and her getting Mercurochrome.*

Q. *How did he happen to have the turkey dish?* A. *The dish was bought at Thanksgiving and it was setting there to hold candies. He then grabbed pictures and with a penknife he made criss-cross slices.*

Q. *Did he say why?* A. *He sounded angry and walked out.*

Q. *Was he drinking at that time?* A. *No, he wasn't.*

Q. *Were there other occasions when he broke things up?* A. *Yes. He would pick up glasses and throw them in the sink like that. My brother wanted him carried to Bellevue, but my mother persuaded him not to because she wanted to keep him home. Even the night the cops came she wanted to keep him there because she loved him.*

Q. *In the period of these muggings, did he seem to have*

any unusual amount of money with him? A. All that I could see was that he would buy an occasional soda for himself at the house.

Q. *Did the family know that he had been drinking?* A. A maternal aunt stated that she had never seen him drunk.

Q. *How about girls?* A. He never talked of them. He talked of a Mary somebody but we haven't heard of her in a long time.

Q. *You mean Mary H—?* A. Yes.

Mary H— testified as follows:

Statement by Dr. Cassity: *This is a hearing before the Commission to find out something about personality, habits and behavior of Theodore Samuels, whom we have been led to understand was your friend.* Q. *Where did you meet?* A. I met him at a party in 1946.

Q. *Did you see him on dates or at other parties?* A. No. I saw him only once again at a friend's house.

Questioning by Dr. Herman: Q. *You had only two contacts with him in your life?* A. Yes, until March. I was coming home from my friend's house at about three-thirty or four A.M. When I walked up the steps he was at the door ringing my bell. I said "Of all people, I haven't seen you in such a long time." So he asked me if he could come in. I said "It's so late. I don't want you to come in." He said, "You have to unlock your door anyway." So I un-

locked my door. He then asked me if I had any money and I told him no. So before I knew anything, he had hit me.

Q. *With his fist?* A. *With something, back here (indicating occipital region). I fell and all of a sudden he started beating me on the face. I started screaming and then he started choking me as though he was trying to kill me.*

Q. *Did you have your pocketbook in your hand?* A. *I had a shoulder bag. When he was choking me, my mother got up to go to the bathroom. She is deaf and dumb. When she came to the door, he ran.*

Q. *Did he try to rifle your shoulder bag?* A. *He didn't even try.*

Q. *What did you think of him the first time you met him?* A. *I thought he was a nice fellow.*

Q. *Did he ever make any passes at you?* A. *No.*

Questioning by Mr. Mendelson, counsel for the defense: Q. *Outside the apartment, after he had asked you if you had any money, did he make a grab for your pocketbook?* A. *No.*

Questioning by Dr. Cassity: Q. *Did you tell him that you had no money?* A. *Yes.*

Theodore Samuels, the defendant, testified as follows:

Questioning by Dr. Cassity: Q. *How do you feel today?* A. *Not bad, not bad.*

Q. *You have been here over a month and you have had considerable time to think things over, particularly in re-*

gard to your involvement. Would you care to make any remarks about your feelings? A. *I can't think of anything I want to say at all.*

Questioning by Dr. Herman: Q. *Do you remember seeing me?* A. *I think I do.*

Q. *Do you remember seeing the gentleman at the end of the table?* A. *Yes, he is the District Attorney. . . .*

Q. *Tell me, how did you happen to get arrested?* A. *My father brought the police to the house and after a short while I told them what happened, what I had done.*

Q. *What did they bring the police to the house for?* A. *I was cutting up pictures in the living room.*

Q. *What pictures?* A. *Pictures of my brother's wedding—he and his wife.*

Q. *What were you doing that for?* A. *That is something I don't even know myself. I just took it up and sliced it. I can't explain it.*

Q. *Were you angry at your brother?* A. *No, I just happened to be standing near it and I picked it up and cut it up.*

Q. *What feeling did you have at the time you cut it?* A. *I guess that they thought that I was getting desperate and they went down and got the police. I guess they were getting suspicious—reading the papers and my staying out late. They knew I had served time in France for a killing and they thought I had a criminal mind and that I was perhaps dangerous.*

Q. *How do you know they thought you had a criminal mind?* A. *From what I had done. I jumped on this Mary*

H. and I used to hit my older brother with sticks or anything I could get my hands on.

Questioning by Dr. Lichtenstein: Q. *What made you start these muggings?* A. *The first one I did, the first night, I can't explain to save my life. I had money in my pocket, $15 or $20. I had a job, too. I just happened to be out and I did the first mugging there.*

Questioning by Dr. Herman: Q. *Isn't it true that you approached Mary and asked her for money?* A. *No, I didn't ask her for any money at all. I was buying everything. Why should I ask her for money? I had maybe $20 or $30 left. . . .*

Q. *After the killing?* A. *Something seemed to gnaw at me, in my mind. I can't explain it because I don't have the words. It told me to get a drink and to find an outlet by cutting up pictures.*

Questioning by Dr. Cassity: Q. *What was that something that told you?* A. *Nothing told me. I just had no control. Something was driving me . . . Every night I would come out late, see a woman and accost her. I reached a point where I just wanted to hurt them.*

Q. *What happened to the violent feeling when you went home?* A. *I would take everything out of the drawers, throw it away, tear it up and go to sleep.*

By the conclusion of the hearing, the examiners were decisive in their conviction that the defendant had been psychotic for a number of years prior to the murder. A report was submitted to the Court, stating the diagnosis as schizophrenia (a split in the thought processes between reality and fantasy, resulting in emotional deterioration) and recommending the defendant as a suitable case for commitment to the Matteawan State Hospital for the Criminally Insane. The judge signed the order. No effort was made by the prosecutor to controvert the psychiatric findings.

Samuels remained at Matteawan for approximately ten months. At the end of that period, he was returned to the Tombs on the grounds that he had recovered from a reactive psychosis and was capable of standing trial.

"Reactive" implies a reaction to a situation—in this case the reaction of the accused to the plight in which he found himself, to his consternation over the first degree murder indictment. The fact that he had manifested psychotic behavior long before committing any of the crimes, the murder included, was, at this point, evidently not considered.

The District Attorney's office had instigated the reevaluation. The Court acceded to the request of the District Attorney. Samuels was brought to trial before a lay jury, charged with murder in the first degree and with being responsible for it at the time of the crime.

The courtroom became a divided arena!

Dr. Herman and I maintained our belief that the defendant had been mentally ill for many years.

The prosecution, abiding by the M'Naughten Rules, insisted that he knew the nature and quality of his act at the time of the murder, that he knew it was wrong, and that, further, he was capable of understanding the charges and of making a defense thereto.

Prosecution's opinion was based upon several true observations:

The defendant knew that he was in New York. He recalled walking up York Avenue (the site of the murder), and that he attacked the decedent with wilful and larcenous intent.

He later admitted that he knew this was wrong. But did he? Did he really know that it was wrong? Recalling the weird soliloquy that had been his testimony, I was convinced that he was, in any normal sense, quite out of touch with reality. Furthermore, it was inconceivable to me that he could be feigning insanity. His inane verbalizations were all uttered spontaneously. They could not have been lifted from textbooks or from statements made by other psychotic patients with whom he had been in contact. Dr. Herman and I testified to this effect, but with negative results. The jury decided that the defendant had, at all times, known the nature and quality of his acts and realized they were wrong. The M'Naughten Rules had triumphed. Theodore Samuels was convicted of murder in the first degree and later sentenced to the chair.

But the Court of Appeals had, in the interim, the opportunity to review the case. The decision of the lower court was reversed. The reasons follow:

Quotations from the Decision of the Court of Appeals:

"1. *The admission in evidence of the entire contents of the defendant's hospital record and at Matteawan was in error on the ground that these records contained judicial hearsay.*

"2. *It was error to permit the People's psychiatrists to express an opinion as to the defendant's mental condition basing their opinion on the hospital records inasmuch as these records were not submitted to the jury, nor allowed to be considered by them.*

"3. *The People (the prosecution) failed to establish beyond reasonable doubt that the defendant was sane at the time of the commission of the crime.*

". . . *The two psychiatrists who testified that the defendant was sane, based their opinion in part on the City (Bellevue) records.*

"4. *The error was not harmless. Had the hospital records been properly before the jury (as they should have been, before hypothetical question was posed) its verdict might well have been different. Judgment of conviction should be reversed and a new trial ordered.*"

As a result of this decision, the defendant was returned to the Tombs and subsequently re-committed to Bellevue for re-evaluation.

Legal gymnastics have priority over objective medical conclusions.

Upon re-examination and in the presence of representatives from the office of the District Attorney, the defendant now made the following statements:

The purpose of school is to refresh the soul. Schools don't really belong (pausing) because the reason I say that—two thousand years ago these objects we have now—the physical body—the most adequate survive. Put it in this form: Most people do not have their real objects. What am I saying? Oh, yes, the mind is not able to grasp and we have to have schools. Souls—(you spoke of similar things when you were here before) *It says on the chart—and I had to be put in confinement to be revealed and that is how I know about it. So I searched many libraries through my course in the Army and in Boston for several years, and experience here and there in putting it in my head all my life, I did it, and if I didn't get into this trouble, I can reach in back of these things.*

About the manslaughter in which he had killed a woman overseas, he stated: "It was like a dream. . . . You see, these are real bodies—thought atoms, immovable—and with those injected into me. (By whom?) By unseen people, human beings; they are people—cells—brain cell—microscopic—intelligent beings and these beings are able to carry on and that is why people have special visions."

During the hearing he alluded to events which were destined, he believed, to come to pass before the end of the year. "There will be a world revolution," he predicted, "frightful things. . . . Atmosphere, moisture, terrible serums and so forth; midwaves . . . more to come yet."

As in the previous interviews conducted a year and a half before, the defendant registered little or no emotional reaction; almost everything was colorless, even his statement of dire predictions. This dearth of emotion is characteristic of one of the varieties of schizophrenia. It is unmistakable, especially when accompanied by the fantastic and unrealistic type of ideation as noted in this case.

Following the third and final hearing, the patient was returned to Matteawan. He is still there.

The use of the antiquated values of the M'Naughten Rules and their application by a tribunal of non-professionals, had come perilously close to sending a man, bereft of reason and responsibility, to his execution.

10

Was society at fault?

Last night, I saw him take the last step. I sat 25 feet away as he died in the electric chair at Sing Sing. The 28-year-old pipefitter who was reared by drunken parents went to his death believing that society—and not he—was the real villain. "God knows I was innocent when I was born," he once told a friend, "but they (society) made me a killer. They forgot all about me when I needed help and understanding."

Larry Nathanson, JOURNAL-AMERICAN, 1/27/56

THE MULTIPLE MURDERER and rapist whose case history follows exhibited many of the same anti-social behavior patterns as the "Apeman." Both were calloused, ruthless, and almost demoniacal in their perpetration of many atrocious crimes of violence. Neither was capable of understanding the quality of social and ethical codes and restraints, nor of appreciating the necessity of conforming to them. Their infamous acts were committed repetitiously and without restraint, never attended by any sense of guilt or regret.

But the "Apeman," as already demonstrated, was psychotic. The multiple murderer, John Roche, was suffering from no mental disorder. The origin of his difficulties was evidently his execrable home environment which seemed, almost literally, to push him into juvenile delinquency. He spent most of his boyhood and adolescence in one institution or another. The bitterness this engendered took the form of a hatred of society which, in turn, seemed to shape an attitude of murderous resolve. The result: a series of rape murders, none of which was detected until he confessed to them following his final arrest. Nor were all his crimes committed in the course of rape; more than one was clearly connected with robbery where the victim was a male.

The murder for which he was at last picked up occurred early one morning in the Spring of 1954. Dorothy Westwater, 14, walked out of her second-floor apartment on York Avenue, to go to school. John Roche was waiting for her on the street floor. He stabbed her, ravaged her sexually during her dying moments, and left her to die.

More or less by accident, the attacker was later identified as the "Mass Murderer" or M.M. (so he was already being called by the press) who had left the murder weapon in a stolen car nearby. According to Deputy Inspector Feeley attached to the Manhattan East Detective Squad, the suspect made no effort to deny his guilt and readily confessed having committed several other murders along the same pattern. He also stated that he wished to absolve an innocent man who had been wrongly convicted of killing a sailor in Queens County. The proof that he submitted to the detective, convinced the latter that M.M. had been in the vicinity of that murder at the time of its perpetration.

Irrespective of his admissions of guilt regarding other crimes, the police were stayed, pending the outcome of the York Avenue murder, the only one upon which he had been indicted.

John Roche, at this time, was 27 years of age. He was born in New York City, the older of two siblings; the younger was a girl, 1½ years his junior. Her name was

K. She gave a very revealing account of the familial background and set-up. Some of her statements follow:

My mother died here in Bellevue. That's what the death certificate said. She was a terrible alcoholic. She was that way for 16 years. (Your father?) *He drank heavily too. He died of tuberculosis.* (What do you remember about John?) *Not much until we were sent to Ireland when he was 5 and I was 3½. He lived with his grandmother and I lived with my mother's cousin there. My father died 3 years later and we returned home. Then I remember John pretty well. We were close, chummy, went to school together, played together.* (Was there anything peculiar about his behavior at that time?) *I have never seen anything peculiar in his behavior. He always seemed to be perfectly normal, that is, until he began to get into trouble* (at 12) *when he was sent to Children's Village for truancy and burglary.*

A report from that institution, while mentioning minor physical ailments, such as colds and furunculosis, failed to make allusion to any mental handicap. His intelligence quotient was reported the same as has been found on subsequent tests—dull normal—in the 90's.

The quotation from the sister continues:

He was sent in and out of prison since he was 16. He was in Comstock, Elmira, Woodbourne and Coxsackie penal institutions. (Crimes?) *Petit larceny, burglary, breaking and entering. He had one felony, I think, a car.*

(After he was released from custody?) *He got along well with my husband who was a machine designer, studying also at nights. John seemed to envy, and admire him.*

As to the mother, she recounted:

He didn't like his mother too well. She would beat him unmercifully. She brought men to the house. (Did he seem resentful about this?) *He would never talk about it. He seemed to feel that our mother had let him down. The Wednesday before her death, I wanted to take her to the hospital, but my stepfather objected and she wouldn't cross him. I came back on Friday and no one was there. I tried to see her for a month and one night I found someone else in the apartment and she showed me a telegram saying that my mother had died in Bellevue. She was a very heavy drinker—had the DT's a couple of times. When John was 14 my mother left him alone in a furnished room. She just walked out and left him and was gone for about six months.*

His work record was irregular. Though he never got fired, he was frequently laid off. He walked out on his last one.

When I first saw him in the Tombs (following the instant and last offense) *he broke down and cried and asked me to forgive him. I said "Landa* (a girl friend whose statement follows this one) *wants me to say hello to you for her." He said "What's the matter with her; doesn't she realize what I have done? Tell her to forget* me." (Was he remorseful?) *No, he said he was merely sorry for dragging me into it.* (Did he show any sign of grief or penitence over any of the crimes?) *No. To the contrary, he appeared to fantasize others than himself as being the culprits despite his confessions which he was unaware that I had any knowledge of. For example, he would say "How could a fellow rape a young girl?"* (Yet he admittedly had raped and killed 3 female adolescents). *In addition, he confessed to three other killings in the course of robbery; one, an 85-year old woman; two, a cab driver, and three, the sailor victim in Queens for which another was convicted erroneously. At the Tombs he refused to discuss any of the details of his crimes, merely inquiring about the welfare of relatives and telling about his life on the ward. At one time, however, he made a rather significant if not ominous statement to the effect that "My troubles are over. I only feel badly about you and Robert* (her husband)."

The following statement was made by the last girl friend of the defendant; it is quoted only in fragments.

Q. *How long have you known him?* A. *I was introduced to him last September.* (About a year prior to the last offense.)

Q. *How did he impress you upon first acquaintance?* A. *He seemed friendly, sociable.*

Q. *Did he seem under any emotional tension or anything like that?* A. *Not that I could notice.*

Q. *Did you go out with him steadily or only occasionally?* A. After he came back from Rikers Island in March, we went out steady.

Q. *At that time, did he show any tendency to lose his temper or to fly off the handle?* A. No.

Q. *These various murders to which he has confessed, did he discuss any of them with you at all before?* A. Well, I discussed one with him, that is when I was dating him.

Q. *Which one?* A. The last one that occurred, that one connected with the girl on York Avenue.

Q. *What did he say about that?* A. I mentioned it first. He spoke to me over the phone—just talking to him, had a conversation with him, and I said it was a shame and he agreed.

Q. *Just talking about it like someone else did it?* A. That's right.

Q. *What led to your breaking up?* A. I don't know. He ran out on me. He was out with some fellow and he said that they had been in an automobile accident and he said he had been drinking. He also said that he had been taking Benzedrine (a stimulant purported to alleviate depression, to bring one out of the "doldrums"). I told him that I did not like the idea of that. He said that he took them to sleep. (Actually, this drug tends to increase sensitivity rather than inhibit it.)

Q. *Did you indulge in sexual relationships?* A. Not completely. We got to a certain stage, that is all.

Q. *Did you discuss having sexual relations?* A. We discussed it. He mentioned doing things like that and I told *him no because I was not raised to do things like that.*

Q. *In your conversation with him, did he at any time make statements that sounded bizarre or irrational?* A. *Not that I can remember.*

Q. *The last time that you saw him was about a week before the crime?* A. *That's right, about a week.*

Q. *What was your reaction when you heard about the tragedy?* A. *I was horrified. I became very ill and my mother became very ill and everybody did. I simply couldn't believe it.*

Q. *Did he ever express any ideas that could be construed as queer or abnormal?* A. *He mentioned a book to me once by a doctor named Fink, called "Relaxing from Nervous Tension."*

Q. *Did he seem to be under nervous tension since you made acquaintance with him?* A. *He said once that he had a twitch in the face which I have never noticed.*

Up to this point, there had been no evidence of psychotic thinking, emotivity, or behavior.

Nor were there any indications of psychosis in the picture of the defendant as I saw him on several occasions.

From the very beginning, he seemed rational, cooperative, and usually complacent. On occasion, he was observed by the night nursing shift to grow restless around midnight, pacing up and down in his cell, constantly smoking cigarettes. But he required no sedation after his first few days in the institution. According to the nurses' notes and my own personal observations, he was inclined to be quite sociable with the other inmates, participating freely in conversations and games with them. He had one minor quarrel with another patient about television. During our personal interviews, he made no attempts to dissimulate.

Here are some samples of his statements:

Q. *How old were you when you first went to an institution?* A. 12.

Q. *Then, since you were 12, how much time have you spent in prisons or other penal institutions?* A. *Well, it started when I was about 12 and now I been in about 8½ or 9 years* (i.e., intermittently between the ages of 12 and 26. He was 27 at the time of his admission to Bellevue.)

Q. *Around or about the time that the first murder incident occurred, did you notice any change in yourself?* A. *No, that was about August last year.*

Q. *Now, when you made a confession to that one, was it under pressure?* A. *No.*

Q. *Then how did they come to get hold of you?* A. *They picked me up in Rockaway with a stolen car.*

Q. *Were you drinking at the time?* A. *No.*

Q. *Then what was the motive that was going through your mind?* A. *I don't know. I just wanted to rob him.*

Q. *That was the sailor?* A. *Yes.*

Q. *Did he resist you?* A. *No. He was asleep and he woke up and I just hit him with the pipe I had.*

Q. *Were you angry?* A. *I don't know how I felt.*

Q. *Ever have tendencies like that before to strike somebody?* A. *Yes, at times, if somebody got me mad, but not for no reason.*

Q. *Never got so mad that you felt like killing?* A. *No.*

Q. *Tell us about the second one?* A. *It was around the fall or early winter of 1953* (the year previous to the present one). *I was burglarizing an apartment and the woman woke up, so I stabbed her.*

Q. *Did you take the knife with you?* A. *Yes, I went and got the knife out of the kitchen first.*

Q. *It was an old woman?* A. *Yes, she was about 85.*

Q. *Where did you go after this happened?* A. *I don't know. I remember I was pretty well loaded but I remembered what I was doing. I felt that there was something wrong with me and I hinted to my sister that I would like to see a psychiatrist, but I did not know how to go about it.*

Q. *Did you have assaultive tendencies before last year?* A. *Yes, they had been going on since I was 16.* (11 years).

Q. *Was that the first time you stabbed somebody?* A. *Yes.*

Q. About how many stabbings or beatings would you say you administered? A. I have no idea.

Q. What was the motive? A. Robbery, yes.

Q. What was the most money you obtained from the stabbings and beatings? A. Not much, $10 or so.

As to the third case, he admitted that the murder was committed in the course of rape.

Q. *What was going through your mind when you attacked this 17-year old girl?* A. *It was in a hall. I had seen her in the neighborhood, but I didn't know her. One day I followed her into the hall. I wanted to talk to her,* but she ignored me and she started to go upstairs. I had a knife with me and I stabbed her in the back.

Q. What were you doing with the knife? A. I always carried it; for things like if I was going to burglarize a house, something for protection.

Q. But burglary had nothing to do with this case? A. I had been burglarizing steady. I usually took a knife if I was going to do a burglary or a robbery. I had to have a weapon.

Q. Did you feel that somebody was out to get you? A. No.

Q. You stabbed the girl in the hallway. Then what happened? A. Then I was going to rape her.

Q. Try to rape her first or stab her first? A. Stabbed her first.

Q. What was going on in your mind? A. Because I didn't want her to resist.

Q. Did you rape her? A. No, I attempted to.

Q. Did you have an erection? A. Yes.

Q. What happened? A. So somebody—I heard some people on the ground floor moving around and I heard someone call another person. I heard the door open and I ran out.

Q. Would you please tell us about the next one? A. The cab driver was next.

Q. Did you stab him? A. Yes.

Q. Because he resisted you? A. Yes, because I was going to rob him.

Q. Where was this? A. This was down here on 22nd Street. It was about 4 o'clock in the morning.

Q. He resisted you and you stabbed him—where? A. First in the back and then he turned around and I stabbed him in the stomach. Then I went off.

Q. How did you feel at that time? A. I felt bad, and I didn't know what to do. I didn't want to give myself up.

Q. The last murder that you admitted having connection with, occurred on York Avenue? A. Yes.

Q. You didn't know that girl? A. No. It was early in the morning. A little after 8.

Q. She was going to school? A. Yes, that was lust—I had a knife and a pipe.

Q. When you entered the hallway and found her—did you have any intention of having sexual intercourse? A. No. I was down in the back yard—and I was going to burglarize a house and I kept a pipe and a knife with me so that if somebody gave me some resistance I could use them as a weapon. I went up and down the yard—yards are connected with other yards, and go quite a distance—anyway most of the windows were screened, so I couldn't. I came back and was coming up the hall, when this kid was ready to go out in the street.

Q. Was she attractive? A. Yes. Then it hit me that I wanted to rape her.

Q. Did you have an erection at the time? A. No, then I hit her with the pipe first.

Q. On the head? A. Yes, I hit her a couple of times.

Q. Get pleasure out of it even though she was unconscious? A. Yes.

Q. Was she unconscious when you raped her? A. Yes.

Here, as always, we see an unconscionable determination to avenge himself upon a society which had stacked the cards, so to speak, against him at the very outset of his existence. His selections of victims were distinctly vicarious ones, and could in no way be charged to personal venom. He had never made the acquaintance of any of the decedents. His murderous acts were apparently conceived and perpetrated impulsively and indiscriminately, and did not emanate from delusional thinking.

At the formal hearing, he volunteered statements which led to the same conclusion. The following experts were present at the hearing:

For the State:

Dr. John H. Cassity, Psychiatrist-in-Charge of the Criminal Service, Dr. Benjamin Apfelberg, Assistant Director of the Psychiatric Unit, Dr. Theodore S. Weiss, an officially designated examiner, Dr. Morris Herman, Professor of Psychiatry at Bellevue Medical Center, Mr. Alexander Herman, Assistant District Attorney in charge of Homicide, and Mr. Robert Reynolds, his assistant.

For the Defense:

Mr. James D. C. Murray, one of our most distinguished trial lawyers, was appointed by the Court to defend the accused. He was assisted by the able attorney, Mr. Abraham J. Gellinoff.

The first witness called was Deputy Inspector Edward

T. Feeley, a member of the Police Department of the City of New York, attached to the Manhattan East Detective Squad. The Inspector was the arresting officer in this case. He had also been conducting investigations of the other Manhattan murders to which the defendant had confessed but these were not referred to at the hearing.

The questioning and answering proceeded:

By Dr. Cassity: Q. *As you probably know, Inspector, the main interest that we have in holding this hearing and getting a statement from you, is to find out something about this defendant's behavior at the time of his arrest, and any other information you would care to give us regarding his general mental attitude. Would you give us a brief statement, please?* A. *In my observation of the defendant, I didn't notice, in my opinion, any abnormalities. I would say that he showed no remorsefulness and I didn't witness any particular emotion. I did notice a mannerism of a soft speaking voice. During the time I was in his presence he seemed to be concerned with two things. First: He didn't want to be photographed. And he had asked me on the arrival back from Rockaway if I would protect him from being photographed by newspapermen. I asked him why and he just said that he didn't want his picture in the paper. The next thing I noticed about him that seemed to run consecutively, was that he was averse to telling his story more than once. He was required to tell his story a few times. On each occasion it would be necessary to have it repeated. He would* say "Well, do I have to tell this again? I have already told it." That, gentlemen, is about the summation of my observation of his reactions.

Q. Was there any difference in his reactions when you had occasion to see him a few days later? A. I would say no.

By Dr. Weiss: Q. Did he give any reason for not wanting his picture in the paper? A. No, sir, he did not.

By Dr. Cassity: Q. During the course of your conversations with him, did he express any ideas that you would regard as odd or peculiar? Would you say that his conversation was in any way out of the ordinary? A. No, I wouldn't say that it was different from the average individual. I might add that I gathered the impression that he was sort of resigned to his fate.

By Dr. Herman: Q. I would like to know what caused his reluctance to give his story to you? Why was that? Was there any special reason why he was reluctant to do it? A. He wasn't reluctant to tell his story. He was reluctant to repeat it.

Q. How many times did that happen? Did he do that more than once? A. Yes, when I originally arrived there (In Queens) I spoke to him and told him that he was to speak to New York detectives. I said "Tell me about the story." He said, "Do I have to tell it again? I already told them."

Q. How many times did you ask him to tell his story? A. Just in relation to our particular clients here in Manhattan? You see there is another phase to this investigation that originated in Queens.

Q. *In relation to all of them?* A. *I presume about eight times.*

Q. *Tell me, was he excited at any time during the repetitions?* A. *Never at any time that I spoke to him, Doctor.*

Q. *Did he come out with any peculiar expressions which indicated his anger or resentment toward any of the people of his last victim?* A. *No, sir.*

Q. *Did he indicate in any way that he was recalling imaginary voices? Those that he would hear that were not discernible by anyone else?* A. *No, sir.*

Q. *He responded to questions quickly, would you say?* A. *I wouldn't say quickly. I would say normally.*

Q. *And his answers were responsive to the questions given?* A. *Yes, sir. With one exception. He would go along and sometimes in an answer he might come to a certain point of it, and if you tried to pin him on that particular point, he would say "I don't remember" or, "Maybe." His answers in general were quite complete.*

Q. *Did you have the impression that his memory was faulty?* A. *My impression was that his memory was quite good.*

By Dr. Weiss: Q. *Did you think it unusual, or not, that he admitted to other cases?* A. *There was nothing unusual about it; about his admitting it. Some talk and some admit.*

The next witness was the defendant.

By Dr. Cassity: Q. *I am well aware of the fact that you are sick and tired of being asked further questions after so many previous examinations. I will try to make it as brief as possible in order to make it easy upon you. You of course understand that this is a formal hearing to determine something about your feelings and your general reactions and behavior. You don't object to my asking questions?* A. *Do I have to go through that thing again?*

Q. *As I explained to you before, I am going to make it as brief as possible. I told you in advance that what you are here for has nothing to do with your guilt or non-guilt, or anything connected with the present crime. This is merely an effort to determine something about your feelings and ways of thinking. We will not have to go through with all the things we went through before in regard to the alleged offense. Is that all right?* A. *Yes.*

Q. *Were you born in Portchester, New York?* A. *Yes.*

Q. *And your sister is how much younger than you are?* A. *About two years.*

Q. *How old were you when you started to school?* A. *About 5 or 6.*

Q. *I understand that you were about 5 when you lost your father?* A. *About 5. I don't remember anything about this until I was about 7 or so, when I was in Ireland.*

Q. *Was that at the house of your mother's sister?* A. *That was at the house of my grandmother, my mother's mother.* (He was not at all responsive to questions regarding his life with his grandparents between the ages of 5 and 9. He merely alluded to it as "*just a trip over there, you know; I remember that I wanted to come back.*")

Q. *When you came back to the United States, you*

started to live with your mother; and who else? A. My mother and my sister.

Q. *How did things seem to be going when you got home?* A. It was all right at first for a year or so.

Q. *After the first year or so, what happened?* A. We moved to a different apartment and my mother started drinking and we had a lot of arguments.

Q. *Did she become abusive?* A. Yes.

Q. *Then you would say that your life after you returned to your mother was not very pleasant?* A. No.

Q. *Then, concerning your mother's behavior; were there other things that happened that were not so good, possibly immoral?* A. Yes.

Q. *Will you tell us about that, please, briefly?* A. Yes. She used to have men come up to the house. Drunken affairs.

Q. *Would they have sexual intercourse in your presence or in the presence of your sister?* A. Not exactly in the presence. Sometimes when we got up in the room they would be naked in bed.

Q. *What were your feelings about it at that time?* A. The feeling was disgusting.

Q. *You returned from Ireland before you started to get into trouble? And you arrived back when you were about 9?* A. About that.

Q. *Did your mother have trouble getting a job?* A. Yes.

Q. *You felt that you were deprived; that you were not getting what you should as far as food and clothes were concerned?* A. Yes.

Q. *Was it about that time that you began to develop a*

feeling of resentment over the fact that you were not getting what the other kids got? A. Sure.

Q. *Did it have anything to do with your getting into trouble like beginning to steal and that sort of thing?* A. I know it had a lot to do with my staying out of the house. There were times when I didn't want to come home at all. I was young and I didn't have no place to go.

Q. *When you first began to steal, was that the result of what was going on in the home or from association with other kids?* A. I think it was from the other kids.

Q. *What form did the stealing take?* A. Pocketbooks, any little things.

Q. *Would you take the money out of the pocketbooks or steal things that you could pawn?* A. No, not that. If I stole a bike, I would use it for a while. Or like skates, whatever it was.

Q. *How old were you when you first got in conflict with the law?* A. About 12. I remember burglarizing a club.

Q. *Was that the crime on which you were sent to Children's Village?* A. Yes.

Q. *How did you get along with the kids there?* A. I got along all right.

Q. *You didn't get in trouble at Children's Village?* A. A few times; I mean nothing serious.

Q. *How long did you remain at Children's Village?* A. Two years.

Q. *Did you continue school in those two years?* A. I continued school.

Q. *Then how much later did you start to get in trouble again?* A. About 16.

Q. Then your activities against law and order took on a different form at that age? A. When?

Q. Before, you would just pick up a pocketbook or a watch. Then you say your performance took on more serious aspects, such as carrying certain weapons around? A. Yes.

Q. What was going through your mind when you got hold of a knife? A. No answer.

Q. Will you tell the gentlemen here what was in your mind at the time of your criminal acts? A. None.

Q. I think that you used an expression "If I got caught, it would be either him or me." Do you remember using that expression? A. That is what I meant, to get away with it, if I had to use it.

Q. Later on some other things started happening where you started to feel that you would have to use it? A. Yes, after I came out of Comstock. (One of the state prisons.)

Q. At what stage of the game did sex come into the activities? There were incidents that you mentioned when you would go with girls by forcing them at the point of a knife? A. At about 16.

Q. Would you do it if they resisted you? A. Only when they resisted me.

Q. Would you have erections at the time of the attacks? A. Yes.

Q. Did they occur before or after it? A. They occurred during the attack.

Q. Would you feel sorry about these activities? A. Sometimes, and then I would drink some and start to cry.

Q. Were you angry when you would make the attacks?

A. *Once or twice I was. I had a feeling that I have to defend myself if I'm going to get what I'm going after, and I thought I may have to hit them with something.*

Q. *Did you ever feel that, now, I am on the downtrodden track, being chased around in institutions and no real home, I don't give a damn as far as society is concerned?* A. *Yes, I think I told you that. I knew eventually that I would get caught. I just didn't care.*

Q. *How do you feel now about these crimes you have allegedly committed?* A. *I feel bad. In a way, I don't feel bad. In other words, I can't do anything. It is over.*

Q. *Do you think that it was possible for you to have resisted these urges?* A. *Most of the time I was out of work. Like when I stole the $25 from a guy, if I had a job and could adjust myself like other people, it could have been avoided. I was actually driven to steal at times. The reason I killed them was that I didn't want to be identified or get caught.*

Q. *That is the same reason, I believe, that you gave for not going to a psychiatrist; because you feared detection?* A. *Yes.*

Q. *And was not that the same reascn you did not discuss the situations with your sister or your girl friend?* A. *Yes.*

Q. *At any time, did you ever have an idea that someone was out to frame you, or cause you trouble?* A. *No.*

Q. *Was there ever a time that you thought you heard something happening, when there was actually nothing there?* A. *No.*

Q. *Possibly, on occasion, you noticed people eyeing you on the street?* A. *I don't remember anything like that.*

The questioning by Dr. Weiss, my associate, corroborated my findings that the defendant was not suffering from a psychosis, but was a victim of dire environmental circumstance. Dr. Herman, also for the People, was unable to elicit any psychotic ideation. A male friend and contemporary of the defendant, testified:

We used to go to the beach together and he would stay with the crowd that was with us. He seemed to tell the truth. As to arguments, he would walk away and come back later. (Exchange confidences with you?) *Never. He did say that he was tired of going to prison and was thinking of going in the Merchant Marines. He mixed, but he didn't exchange confidences.*

The minutes of the hearing go on:

By Mr. Murray: Q. *John, do you know who I am?* A. *Yes, you are James D. C. Murray.*

Q. *Were there not lawyers assigned to defend you?* A. *Yes.*

Q. *Do you want them to defend you?* A. *Yes.*

Q. *Do you want them to exert their efforts to save you from murder conviction. Do you want them to do that?* A. *I don't know how you can.*

Q. *I will ask you something else; do you care whether you live or die?* A. *No, not now.*

Q. So you want to die? A. *No, I don't want to die, but I would rather die than to spend the rest of my life in jail.*

Q. *In other words, you would rather die than be sent to a jail or a mental institution. Is that right?* A. *Yes.*

Q. *If there is a trial, would you be willing to testify?* A. *Me testify? For what?*

Q. *In your own defense, would you take the witness stand and testify in your own defense?* A. *What is the sense of that?*

Q. *Now, John, I have been breaking my back to save your neck. Do you, or do you not, want to cooperate with me in my effort to save you from the Chair?* A. *The entire thing is hopeless. I told them everything. They will convict me on everything that I told them.*

Mr. Murray: I have no further questions.

And so, John F. Roche, M.M., Mass Murderer, victim not of delusion or fantasy but of overpowering environmental factors, went to his death in Sing Sing's electric chair on the night of January 25, 1956. His only regret, he said, was that he had killed the wrong people.

The pretense of insanity

Mad-Dog Murderers Carried to Electric Chair Still Feigning Insanity . . . Anthony and William Esposito, who at their trial almost a year ago were termed the most vicious killers ever to walk the streets of New York, have paid with their lives for a career of crime that was culminated January 14, 1941 by the cold-blooded slaying of . . . .

SUN, 3/13/42

AT HIGH NOON, on a Winter day in 1941, the two Esposito brothers engaged in open gunfire at one of New York's most congested intersections, 5th Avenue and 34th Street. They killed an unarmed linen store manager, a resisting payroll-bearer, and a patrolman, and gravely wounded a taxicab driver.

They began with a payroll stickup. After shooting the payroll-bearer, they sauntered through a large department store with the payroll bag in their possession. They followed, quite calmly, the pattern of the crowd so as not to arouse suspicion or create a panic, and made their way to the 5th Avenue exit. But here, they were met by the police who had been alerted via S.O.S. signals. A police shot wounded one of the brothers. The officer who had fired the shot was quickly killed. At the point of a gun, the brothers then commandeered a cab. The driver, sizing up the situation, hesitated just one moment too long at a green light. This nearly cost him his life. One of the trigger-happy Espositos let him have it. The driver lived, however, to tell the tale, and his unwelcome passengers were immediately overpowered by a swarm of police.

Since one of the brothers had sustained a slight wound, both were sent to Bellevue for physical check-up. Later, because of their antics and lack of cooperation, a formal commitment was received from the Court, ordering a psychiatric evaluation, as well.

Potentially, these two "mad-dog" killers seemed to me adjustable human beings. It is even conceivable that their life of crime might have been altogether averted had they been exposed to a different environment and conditioned, at an early age, to constructive education. The background from which they came was one of absolute squalor and viciousness. Data was obtained from (1) the records of the Public School; (2) Probation Bureau of the Court of General Sessions; (3) an interview with the "girl friend" of the older brother; (4) a statement made by their sister and (5) from records of the Social Service Exchange Clearance.

The older sister recounted that the father had served a prison sentence in Bayonne, New Jersey, for fighting with a "crazy" brother of the mother. She later reported that he, the father, had administered severe beatings to both brothers following minor infractions in conduct. She attributed the difficulties of the whole family to the mother. She described the latter as follows: "She talks crazy sometimes and screams, blood pressure, you know, goes to the head." She also stated that she had another brother who was "crazy" and who used to stab people and that he had been in prison and had hanged himself in Ohio. Another, a fourth brother, was in Dannemora Prison at the time of the instant offense, for a parole violation. The father's mother, she said, died in a "crazy house" in Palermo, Italy. She described the older defendant as "a poor student and a wild kid, playing truant and fighting." She further reported that he would never stay at home and that the neighbors frequently complained about his belligerency.

She was unable to supply many details about the early life of the younger brother. She recalled that he was unconscious at one time—during his adolescence—when he was sentenced to a seven and one half to fifteen year term in prison. She attributed the unconscious reaction to the severe thrashings he had received from the father.

The "girl friend," the woman with whom the older of the defendants had been living in a common-law relationship for four months prior to the arrest, was interviewed at great length. From her description of his behavior, his reactions towards her, and his day-to-day relationship with her, nothing was noted to indicate that he was behaving in any abnormal fashion.

The following is a record of the older defendant's previous arrests: Children's Court, 1921 (20 years prior to the crime); Juvenile Delinquency, Special Sessions Court, 1924; discharged on petit larceny charge in 1925 and sent to New York City Reformatory for six months; escaped October 26, 1925; March 1926, sentenced to from 5 to 10 years in Sing Sing Prison on a charge of attempted robbery, 1st degree; paroled to Ellis Island on a deportation warrant; escaped on July 12, 1930.

The criminal record of the younger brother dated back to 1921 when he was arrested on a charge of robbery. He resisted being taken into custody by attempting to fire an automatic loaded pistol at the arresting officer. While being subdued by a blow on the head from an officer's gun, he called out to his two companions: "Come on, give it to him." He was sentenced to from 7½ to 15 years in a state prison. Three years later, in 1932, he was transferred to Great Meadows Prison where less punitive measures are invoked. Here, he was described as a model prisoner. Statements of commendation were made regarding his exemplary behavior by the Warden, the prison physician, the Catholic Chaplain and the prison psychiatrist, Dr. Foxe, who, incidentally, appeared as a witness in his behalf at the murder trial. None of these officials, including the physicians, made any mention of psychotic manifestations, and as a result of their appraisals he was paroled to the custody of his sister in January of 1936. During that year, he was arrested on four different occasions, but because of lack of evidence he was reinstated on parole. In November of 1937, information came to the Parole Division that he had been involved in a hold-up. He was alleged to have shot at a policeman who had attempted to apprehend him. Information also came to the detectives that he was willing to give himself up if the Parole Board would only allow him another year's extension of the parole. The request was apparently granted for he was at large up until the time of the 1941 mass murders.

My original impression, that neither he nor his brother was ever mentally ill, was supported by the statement of the older brother's "girl friend" to the District Attorney. Extract from the D.A.'s report:

Informant lived with the older of the defendants for four months as his common-law wife. . . . She stated that she saw the younger brother occasionally when he would come to the house and that he always talked very kindly to her. She never saw him act strangely, never saw him looking suspicious, or heard him tell his brother that anyone was after him. On the day of the instant offense she saw him and noticed no unusual behavior.

A communication from Warden Lawes, Sing Sing Prison, read as follows:

Replying to your letter of February 17th relative to (the younger defendant), *this is to inform you that he was locked up on January 7, 1932, on suspicion of being implicated in the murder of #82640, which occurred November 12, 1931. He was placed in the detention cell on January 7th, 1932, for reasons of segregation and was transferred to the center wing of the condemned cells February 5th, 1932. He was tranferred to Great Meadows Prison on December 19th, 1932.* (For the reasons stated earlier.) *During his incarceration he showed no signs of depression or insanity and always cooperated with the officials.*

Shortly after their commitment to Bellevue for mental observation, the brother defendants appeared to be suddenly and simultaneously stricken with mental aberration. The numerous attempts made to examine them verbally met with little success. Their responses to questions were usually evasive, and delivered with non-informative "I don't knows" or "I can't remember." More often, no answers were given.

We then decided to resort to the "truth serum." The use of this serum—a barbiturate—acts upon certain nerve centers in such a manner as to remove both inhibitions and those defense mechanisms ordinarily utilized to insure self-preservation.

The drug was first administered intravenously to the elder brother. Under its influence he talked very freely and related incidents in his life which had taken place prior to his arrest. All of his statements were rational and coherent. Giving added support to our suspicion of dissimulation was the behavior of the defendant a short while later, but long after the effects of the sedative had worn off. To mention a specific incident, he took a hard boiled egg which he had been given for breakfast, placed it on the floor, and on his hands and knees pushed it around with his nose. On another occasion he peeled an orange, ate the peel, discarding the fruit. When taking a shower, he put soap in his mouth but did not chew it, and then removed it from his mouth.

Under the narco-synthesis, the younger co-defendant displayed a reaction similar to that observed in his brother. There was no evidence of memory impairment or confusion as to his whereabouts. (Little was delved into regarding the crime. The determination of guilt or innocence is exclusively the province of the Court and the jury. Our psychiatric function is to pass upon the ability or inability of a defendant to understand the charges against him and of making a defense thereto.)

This younger defendant, at first, non-committal, later agreed to make responses to questions in writing. He wrote as follows: "I am Sir John Garibaldi." He then snatched the piece of paper upon which he had been writing, tore it to pieces and pushed them into his mouth. He then wrote on another slip: "Don't talk in the enemy's camp."

From the evidence thus far adduced, it became quite obvious to the examiners that both defendants were feigning insanity and deliberately so. The reports rendered to the Court indicated as much. The Court decided that both of the culprits were capable of making a defense for themselves if they so wished. They were put on trial for murder in the first degree.

The Trial

By this time both of the defendants had become totally uncommunicative. They did not limit this attitude to the psychiatrists for the State. They refused similarly to cooperate either with their own attorneys or with the expert medical witnesses retained in their behalf. Even the defense counsel admitted the facts of the crime as presented by Mr. Grumet, the Assistant in charge of the Homicide Branch of the office of the District Attorney, Mr. Thomas E. Dewey. Mr. Tell, the chief counsel for the defense did, however, maintain (Quoted from the minutes of the trial):

I will prove to you not only by heredity, environment, but by actual medical testimony in this court, by a doctor who examined these defendants 7 years ago up in a state institution. He will tell you what the report was about these defendants years back, when these boys were juvenile delinquents. . . . And that ever since their inception and introduction into crime in New York, that these boys have been mental cases and that after I have proven to you that they did not know the nature and consequence of their act, I want you to render an honest and fair verdict and have the courage of your conviction.

He made further attempts to bolster his defense by reference to hereditary factors which had already been amplified in the Bellevue report.

Mr. Tell's approach was impressive. Its momentum, however, was unquestionably dissipated in the eyes of the jury by the testimony of Dr. Foxe, who had seen both of the defendants, about 7 years previous to the proceedings, in state institutions. The doctor, after many hours of direct and cross-questioning, was unable to make a definite statement regarding the degree of mental responsibility possessed by either defendant on the day of the crime. His colleague, Dr. Mittleman, was equally equivocal in his rather weak protestations regarding their responsibility. He refused to express a specific opinion concerning the mental condition of either defendant at the time of the crime. On the other hand, the psychiatrists representing the prosecution were distinctly emphatic and unanimous in their conclusion that both of the accused were deliberately dissembling.

During the trial, neither of the defendants gave any sign of realizing that his life was at stake. The younger brother sat in a rigid posture, never taking his eyes off the table, except to appear to listen when important witnesses were testifying. The older one continually rotated his head, emitting grunting sounds reminiscent of a famished pig. At one point in the trial, the courtroom was thrown into an uproar to a degree that prompted the Judge to call a recess. The elder of the prisoners had suddenly smeared his face with excreta which he had concealed in his pocket. The Judge issued a stinging rebuke from the bench.

The jury did not tarry long in its deliberation. It returned a verdict of "Guilty of murder in the first degree as asked in the indictment."

In passing sentence, the Court stated ". . . both of the brothers and co-defendants, feigned insanity according to the believable testimony in the case." His conviction that both were sane was based upon certain reports, which, he said, "I am making a part of the record." These had been submitted by Dr. Perry M. Lichtenstein, psychiatrist attached to the District Attorney's office, Dr. Andrew J. Torre, resident physician at the City Prison, and Drs. John H. Cassity and Walter Bromberg, psychiatrists of the General Sessions Court Clinic. In this report, we concluded that "We find the individuals to be not insane, and to be in a mental state that started in a process of malingering and which was engrafted upon it at this time, some hysterical neurotic elements arising out of fear."

While there is little doubt that these defendants knew the nature and quality of their acts at the time of the offense, I doubt very seriously that they were capable of comprehending the significance of accepted social and ethical codes. This moral warping does not absolve them of responsibility. Through their almost daily examples of depravity and corruption in their formative years, they seemingly got the idea that the anti-social way was the "right" one, the "normal" way to eke out an existence. This, in itself, does not reflect a fundamental mental incapacity. What it does reflect is a sad deficit in our cultural development. If this and similar criminal acts were exonerated merely on such grounds, our present-day society would rapidly disintegrate into a veritable chaos.

It is to avoid this disintegration that experts are employed by state and defense. Detachment in judgment and impartiality in opinion are possible only when knowledge and understanding serve as guides in the evaluating process. The role of the expert is actually one of dedication of his specialized skills and his objective thinking to the public interests which he serves.

12

A possessive woman's compulsion

The first woman ever charged with the first-degree murder of another in Brooklyn was placed on trial yesterday in County Judge Leibowitz' Court and fell hysterical to the floor.

MIRROR, 4/2/46

MRS. ESPERANZA PISANTI, 49, who shot and killed Nancy Catalano, a younger woman with whom she had been living, was another example of a malingerer. The circumstances of the case were quite unusual.

The shooting took place in the late Spring of 1942. The victim, hovering always near death, lived until 1946. Her death, at that time, was a direct result of the shooting.

In opening his case, the District Attorney made the following statement:

Let me take you back to 1937, 1938, and let me show you that X, the deceased, and her husband and their three children lived together on S Street in Brooklyn. And at or about this time the defendant penetrated herself, brought herself into the lives of these people. She took over his wife, and a close relationship ensued. She took the deceased and her children to Ozone Park and there they lived together for about three years. And at or about this time we will show you that X, the deceased, desired for the sake of the children, to go back to her husband and do away with this relationship. And at or about this time she started to see her husband on occasions, secretly, and at the homes of relatives. Upon learning this, the defendant continuously threatened to kill the decedent —either she would possess her or she would die.

This contention was substantiated later by a female witness who was acquainted with both the defendant and the deceased. She stated under oath that she had heard the defendant threaten the deceased with the menacing remark that "if you go back to your husband, I will kill you."

The trial got under way before a Blue Ribbon jury. Mrs. Pisanti remained comparatively calm until the daughter of the deceased was put on the stand. Then, as the play-by-play account of the murder began vividly to emerge, the defendant burst out into screams.

The Court ordered a recess. Dr. Gladys McDermaid, a criminal psychiatrist from Kings County Hospital, examined the defendant. Dr. McDermaid's testimony stated that the reactions were merely "hysterical." Further observation at Kings County Hospital seemed, to the Court, to be advisable. But the hospital prison Service for Females was temporarily closed.

I was called into the situation by Judge Leibowitz as an emergency. The question that needed to be decided, as quickly as possible, for the Judge and jury was: "Did she possess and retain sufficient awareness of the proceedings to confer with counsel and make a defense for herself?" If so, the trial would continue; if not, the Court would be obliged to order her commitment to Bellevue for further observation. In the event that she was found mentally ill, she would be confined to the Matteawan State Hospital for the Criminally Insane.

I spent virtually the entire week-end examining Mrs. Pisanti. I found her in a camisole, the canvas jacket which restrains the movements of the arms. Her behavior during the admitting procedures had made this necessary.

She glared at me wildly when I asked her name, began to thrash about in the restraint jacket, shouting, "Mama mia, mama mia, what are they doing to me?" All attempts to establish contact with her through the question and answer method proved futile. She made no response to questions about her name, age, place of birth, marital status, etc. Occasionally, she cried out, "Swear to God." Then she lapsed back into the "mama mia" talk. The staff advised me that she ate and slept regularly and, at times, asked for water.

I needed to decide: Was Mrs. Pisanti really mentally sick? Or was she only trying to convince me with an act, in which she played the role of someone unaware of her identity and whereabouts and unable to comprehend any questions?

I changed my methods of examination. The restraint jacket was removed. When she least expected me, I appeared suddenly behind her bed, making quick requests of her. For example, I asked her to let me see her tongue, open her eyes widely, or extend her right arm. She complied with these requests. Then, just before one meal was to be served, I remarked to the nurse in the hall outside her door, "I don't think that Mrs. Pisanti wants to eat now." Immediately, she cried out, "I eat, I eat."

Despite these unmistakable indications of consciousness at the reality level, the defendant continued her repetitious drivel when confronted with pertinent interrogations about her personal life and affairs. I was convinced that she was simulating psychosis. And my opinion was bolstered by the fact that during the four years between her crime and the death of her victim, Mrs. Pisanti, while in custody, had manifested no signs whatsoever of any mental disorder.

But before giving my diagnosis, I called into consultation two other experts in the field of criminal psychology. After detailed examinations, my colleagues concurred in my opinion. Mrs. Pisanti was, therefore, returned to the trial room. My colleagues and I were required to be present.

Here are the minutes of the proceedings:

The defendant was brought into the courtroom in a chair. The chair was rolled along the floor on its casters by the court officers. The defendant had a camisole on the upper part of her body. Her feet were also in restraint to keep her from kicking. She moaned and cried "mama mia" continuously.

Dr. John H. Cassity, residing in Manhattan, called as a witness, being first duly sworn by the Clerk, Mr. George Leonard, testified as follows:

By the Court:

Q. *Dr. Cassity, will you please state the nature of your profession.* A. *I am a psychiatrist attached to the Department of Hospitals, New York City.*

Q. *State briefly your qualifications.* A. *I am a graduate of Tulane University, New Orleans. I trained in psychiatry at St. Elizabeth's Hospital, Washington, D. C. Later I was a Fellow of the National Committee for Mental Hygiene. Following that, I was the Director of Mental Hygiene Clinics for the State of New Jersey. For the past 15 years I have been a senior psychiatrist at Bellevue Hospital, New York City.*

Q. *Are you attached to the Psychiatric Division of Bellevue Hospital?* A. *I have charge of the Criminal Service there.*

(My two associates were required to give a similar briefing of their professional backgrounds and experience. To me, this seems a sheer waste of time. All expert witnesses, whether called by the prosecution or the defense, should merely be required to submit to the Court evidence of their qualifications in the form of certificates from the duly constituted authorities in their particular field.)

Q. *Have you examined the defendant?* A. *I have.*

Q. *State when and where.* A. *At Bellevue Hospital, today, yesterday and the day before.*

Q. *When did you first see her?* A. *Day before yesterday at 8:15* A.M.

Q. For how long a period did you examine her? A. I examined her alone for about an hour and a half, and conjointly with the two other doctors who are now in court, for another hour.

Q. State their names. A. Dr. Morris Herman and Dr. Benjamin Apfelberg (both qualified experts in the field of criminal psychiatry and functioning at the top level).

Q. State what your examination disclosed. A. As to the physical examination, she was found to be in good general condition. Her pulse was regular and her reflexes were normal. She complained of pains in the abdomen and palpation of the area failed to reveal any evidence of rigidity, tenderness or masses. The heart tones were of good quality.

Q. Now, as to her mental condition, doctor. A. Pardon me your Honor, may I ask a question?

Q. Surely. A. Do you want me to go into detail or do you want me to give a general impression?

Q. I want you to tell me in what condition you found her mentally. Use your own judgment. Your testimony is for the guidance of the Court. I want to determine just what her mental condition is at the present time so that I may determine whether or not this trial is to proceed. A. I found her in a very excited, agitated state. I made efforts to contact her conversationally, both in English and Italian, inasmuch as she spoke English brokenly. Her responses to all questions regarding name, age, place of birth, etc. were irrelevant. She would shout "Mama mia" or "I don't remember."

Q. *"Mama mia" in Italian means "Mother mine?"*
A. Yes.

(I then rehearsed the examinations made at Bellevue which have been described above.)

Q. *Doctor, is the conduct of this defendant honest?*
A. *I would not like to answer that question because it is not restricted to the psychiatric field.*

Q. *I am trying to put it in simple English. Give us your opinion, doctor, as to whether or not this woman is malingering in this case.* A. *I think there is a large element of malingering in this case.*

The other two members of the Bellevue Psychiatric staff followed me on the stand and corroborated my conclusions. The Court then recessed until the following day.

Before leaving Bellevue the next morning, the defendant again became so obstreperous that the use of the camisole was required. It remained in place during her reappearance in court.

As the evidence pointing to her guilt mounted steadily, Mrs. Pisanti became extremely vociferous, loudly denouncing witnesses produced by the prosecution, as liars. The Judge ordered her gagged. He then recalled me to the stand and again asked me whether I thought her capable of continuing to participate in the proceedings. I replied, "Yes, if she so chooses." In place of her verbal barrages, the defendant's protests against the damaging testimony of witnesses were now indicated by glares at them and violent side-to-side movements of the head. The session was prolonged throughout the day. At about 6 P.M., the Court ordered another recess, and asked us all to return at 7 for a continuation.

Upon resumption of the proceedings, it was evident that something of major importance had occurred. The defense counsel appeared relieved. The defendant looked appealingly at the Judge, intermittently lowering her eyes toward the mouth restraint. Judge Leibowitz then addressed the defendant. He told her that he would have the gag removed if she would promise to come up to the Bench and tell the truth. She nodded vigorously in the affirmative. The mouth contrivance was removed and she walked voluntarily up to the Bench. The Judge asked her if she recognized me (glancing in my direction). She replied immediately, "Yes, he is the head doctor." He then asked her if she trusted me and she said "Yes, he's a nice man." "Well," he continued, "you have heard him testify that he does not think there is anything wrong with your mind. Do you think that there is?" She answered very emphatically that she knew she wasn't "crazy." He then informed her that he understood, through her attorneys, that she was ready to take a plea of guilty of murder in the second degree. She replied that she did.

Now again referring to the minutes:

By the Court: Q. *I want you to understand that if you claim you have any legitimate defense I will accept* any plea, but I will order that the case proceed to a verdict. . . . You know what pleading guilty means, Mrs. X? A. Yes.

Q. If there is anything you don't understand I will be glad to make it clear to you. Do you know what pleading guilty means? A. Guilty means when you do something.

Q. When you plead guilty it means that you are making a confession? A. Yes.

Q. That what the District Attorney's witnesses have said is the truth? A. Yes.

Q. You say you killed this woman and that you intended to shoot and kill her. A. I don't intend to shoot her. She want to shoot me.

Q. No; you cannot plead that way if you say that. (Then addressing the defense counsel): Have you made these things clear to Mrs. X? A. I did.

Q. Has the lawyer explained? A. I will do anything you want.

By defense counsel: Q. I told her upstairs it was not what Your Honor wanted. A. (by defendant) I take back those words.

Q. What words do you take back? A. You say I make a mistake talk like this.

Q. No, I did not say anything of the kind. I simply want to know what the truth is. A. All right.

Q. Did you have this revolver? A. I say that.

Q. I am not asking you to say that. I want to know what the truth is. We will get along better if you just do that. A. All right.

Q. *Whatever the truth is you can tell me if you want. You are not under any duty to do that. If you want to be honest with the Judge—* A. *That is right.*

Q. *The Judge will listen to your lawyer's request that I give you a plea to murder in the second degree; but you can do what you please.* A. *O. K.*

Q. *You want to tell me the truth?* A. *All right.*

Q. *Did you have the revolver?* A. *Yes, I have.*

Q. *How long did you have this revolver?* A. *Eight months when the children find the gun down the street. . . .*

Q. *Now on that night that this terrible thing happened, do you remember the night of the week it was?* A. *The day, the night when I get there is the 4th of May, 1942.*

Q. *The next morning was Tuesday after the shooting?* A. *Sure, that is right.*

Q. *It was around midnight, wasn't it?* A. *That is right.*

If there remains an iota of doubt that an accused is not in full possession of his faculties, the court must be reluctant to accept a plea. This accounts for the close questioning regarding the crime and events leading up to it. The defendant is required to go into minute descriptions of the events and circumstances surrounding the act, including dates, places and people involved in the commission of it. Prior to the trial it had been established that the defendant and the deceased had lived together in a state of strange and unusual intimacy for several years before the tragedy, and that the former had become infuriated when the latter decided to terminate the relationship and return to her husband. Witnesses testified that they had heard Mrs. X threaten to kill the decedent if she ever put this resolution into effect.

On the date of the murder, May 4th, 1942, the defendant learned that Mrs. Y, the victim, planned to escort her children to a church social that evening. After Mrs. Y and her children had left for church, Mrs. X got out her gun from its hiding place and followed them. It seemed apparent that she had decided to carry out the act at the church gathering. Her plan was thwarted, however, by the fact that so many people were milling about and her range of aim was obstructed. She went back to wait for Mrs. Y on the stoop of their house.

Further excerpts from the minutes:

Q. *Did you go to the church before or after the play had started?* A. *At about nine o'clock. I got there after the play had started. The place was filled with people.*

Q. *Were some people standing up there?* A. *Yes; in the front, in the first aisle, lot of people.*

Q. *Were the seats all occupied so that some of the spectators had to stand?* A. *Yes.*

By the Court: *Ask the question in Italian, interpreter. I want to make sure about it.* (Interpreted.) A. *All the seats were occupied and I was not the only one standing up. There were more people standing up.*

Q. *Did you look around the church?* A. *Yes.*

Q. *Did you see Mrs. Y there?* A. Yes, I saw her. She was sitting right side this way; she stand up.

Q. *Did you go out of the church before she did?* A. People started to move out, I go out too, myself.

Q. *Mrs. P, did you go out of the church first?* A. Yes.

Q. *Were you nearer the door?* A. I go down the stairs (Interpreted) Yes.

Q. *When you got down stairs, did you take the train to go home?* A. Yes.

Q. *What train did you take?* A. Grant Avenue.

Q. *Is that the Fulton Street line?* A. They call it Lefferts Avenue.

Q. *Lefferts Avenue and Fulton Street?* A. Yes.

Q. *What station did you get off?* A. Montauk Avenue.

Q. *Then you walked home?* A. Yes.

Q. *To Essex Street?* A. Yes.

Q. *When you got back to Essex Street, did you go upstairs to your house?* A. No.

Q. *You were on the street?* A. Just as I come in Essex Street this way, the taxicab came. She and the children got out. She stopped in front of the gate.

Q. *Where did you have the gun?* A. Over here, inside here.

Q. (Indicating inside of left sleeve) A. Yes.

The Court: *Where is the revolver, please?* (The revolver was produced.)

By the Court: Q. *Mrs. X, will you please show me with this revolver how you had it?* (The defendant puts the gun in the left sleeve with the barrel pointing toward the shoulder and the hilt towards the hand slightly visible at the end of the sleeve.)

Q. *You say you went over to the stoop. Did you go up on the stoop?* A. *No; not got chance. She came this way and stopped in front of the gate. When she come down in the front of me I shoot. That is all. That is the truth and nothing else.*

Q. *Did you intend to kill her?* A. *All right, yes.*

Q. *No, no, none of that. You are not going to say anything to please me. I want the truth.* A. *I got a deed to kill her.*

After considering the facts and the evidence very carefully, Judge Leibowitz decided to accept the plea of guilty despite the manifestations of premeditation on the part of the defendant. He did so on the grounds that there were certain extenuating circumstances of a "biological nature" which tended to temper his estimation of the culpability of the defendant.

Mrs. Pesanti was declared guilty of second degree murder and sentenced to a term of 20 years to life at the Bedford State Prison for Women.

13

A modern Greek tragedy

Dreamy eyed, poetry quoting Harlow Fraden, 20, and his writer friend, Dennis Wepman, 22, were indicted today in record time on first degree murder charges in the weird cyanide-and-champagne cocktail murders of Fraden's parents.

JOURNAL-AMERICAN, 12/8/53

WHEN THE BODIES of a doctor and his school teacher wife were found on the floor of their kitchen, both the police and the press called it a suicide pact. The toxicological report revealed that the champagne they had drunk contained sizeable amounts of Potassium Cyanide. But the detectives were not content with the suicide assumption. There was something more to this case than met the eye, they suspected. They proceeded with their investigation.

Four months later they found the son and his friend Dennis living the "life of Riley" in a New York East side apartment. Initially, they expressed their outrage about the possibility of any suspicion pointing to them. Later, they made full confessions of their guilt. The press, at this point, concluded that Harlow had murdered his parents in order to gain the monies from the will of which he was the sole beneficiary.

Both Harlow and Dennis were committed to Bellevue for observation, apparently on the basis of their peculiar behavior. Harlow displayed unrealistic airs of condescension. Dennis seemed strangely inane.

At Bellevue, neither manifested any outward signs of any actual mental aberration. They complied in the performance of routine procedures, answered all questions in reference to statistical data promptly and coherently.

It was at this point that I began my detailed examination of Harlow Fraden, a necessarily exhaustive examination because of the legal limitations involved. The wording of our present statutes consider a defendant legally insane only if he does not understand the charges made against him, did not realize the nature or quality of his acts at the time they were perpetrated, and did not know they were wrong.

Harlow Fraden was clearly in full possession of his faculties. He knew very well what he was doing. The murder was not only preconceived. It was even planned according to a definite schedule.

But Harlow Fraden scorned any effort on the part of defense counsel to render him exculpable. And he derided any attempts to get him to show that he did or did not know the essentials of the charges or of the morals involved. The question of right and wrong needed, in this case, too, to be relegated to the category of philosophy.

The fact remains, however, that Harlow Fraden is and was suffering from a severe chronic mental disorder which served to trigger the instant tragedy. Fortunately, the Judge and the District Attorney agreed with the psychiatric findings and the case did not go to a jury of laymen, which might have tried to controvert them.

In the course of my examination, I obtained facts about the life of the defendant from ten sources. These were:

1. An aunt, sister of the defendant's mother.

2. An uncle by marriage.
3. A paternal cousin.
4. A classmate at New York University.
5. Dr. Z., a psychiatrist who had examined him previously.
6. Dr. H., who had also examined him before.
7. Prof. Murphy, his chemistry teacher at New York University.
8. Copy of Harlow's will obtained through the courtesy of the office of the District Attorney.
9. Affidavit from the Fire Marshall's office regarding the suspicions about the defendant's setting of fires.
10. An attorney, friend of the co-defendant's father.

Harlow Fraden was born in New York City, an only child. His father was a doctor, a career man, connected with the City of New York. The mother was a teacher for the Board of Education. A paternal uncle was found to have been a patient at Harlem Valley State Hospital since 1911. The present reports from that institution indicate that he is in such a state of mental deterioration as to be unable to give pertinent information regarding himself or his family. The father, according to a maternal aunt, was amiable and peaceful, but inclined to be reticent and seclusive. By way of contrast, she described her sister, his wife, as irritable, irascible and unreasonable, later expressing doubt as to the soundness of her mentation. Her impression was supported by that of a psychiatrist who described her as an "ambulatory schizophrenic."

All of the relatives were unanimous in the opinion that the defendant's home life was indeed a turbulent one. The mother was constantly berating the father for not making more money and for being a failure. Her attempts to convey this idea to her son, however, proved fruitless. He regarded his father as a kindly, sympathetic gentleman, and his mother as an "evil person who, in earlier times, would have been burned as a witch." He further charged that she was a "selfish, conniving wretch." Paradoxically, she was lavishing considerable sums of money upon him continuously. When challenged in reference to this fact, he replied sneeringly, "She did it to gratify her own greedy ambitions through my accomplishments."

According to all available reports, the defendant was always a recluse. He had no friends. Though he joined the Boy Scouts at school, after attending one or two meetings, he lost interest. His parents bragged about his writing of poetry, but were disturbed by the fact that the poems were melancholy. Even before leaving high school, he was wont to toy around with chemical gadgets. The aunt testified that the kitchen was always "a mess with chemicals strewn helter-skelter." She further reported that he usually slept late, keeping the door of his room closed. When his mother upbraided him, he would say, "There she goes again. This goes on all the time." The aunt also disclosed the fact that he never had any girl friends, said that she did not "regard him as masculine." She corroborated the rumor that his mother had frequently called him a "sissy."

A maternal uncle contributed the following information:

I knew him before the age of ten. After that, I was in the Service. He was precocious and had an unusual vocabulary. His conversations were usually adult and his remarks were addressed almost exclusively to people who had reached the age of maturity. I do not feel that his mother was especially responsible for this. He had no playmates. His principal interests were tropical fish and reading books from the library. When I was in the Service, he started collecting insignia. He would beseech me to send him samples of buttons and epaulettes which I could obtain from uniforms. When I returned home, I noticed them on the walls of his room. The stove in the kitchen was ruined by his chemicals. In school he would do well only in the subjects which especially interested him. I never heard of his going with girls.

Apparently his grade school years were relatively uneventful. It was in high school that signs of emotional and intellectual disturbances made their first appearance on the personality horizon. The report from the Guidance Department of the Christopher Columbus High School, covering the period from December 1947 through June 1949, indicated excessive absences, migraine headaches, and lagging in all subjects. With the aid of psychiatric counselling, however, he managed to graduate and to be accepted as a freshman at New York University.

It was at about this time that he was suspected of setting fires in the family apartment. Though he denied starting them, he admitted a thrill in witnessing them. He said "It was exciting. I never thought about it until it dawned upon me that the whole thing might be dangerous."

His ideation seemed already to presage an eventual psychotic break.

In 1953, he graduated from New York University, majoring in chemistry—this, despite the fact that in his first two years he received an average of 85, while in the last two, his rating slipped to 55. Twice he failed to appear for the final examination. Just how the degree was finally awarded is not quite clear. Yet, upon the receipt of it, he immediately lost interest. He told one of his professors that with the money he was going to receive from his grandmother, he would utilize his time to read and write poetry and then, after a year, he would return to chemistry.

It would seem that this rather abrupt scholastic collapse coincided with the major onset of his mental illness. Methodically, and through careful inquiry, he now began to take inventory of notorious homosexual "hangouts," and to frequent them. He admitted promiscuous indulgence in these activities, both actively and passively. Sardonically, he recalled having cohabited with one or two females. "I merely did this to prove that I was homosexual. Looking back, I always knew it." Shortly thereafter, he fell in love with one Dicky, a sailor, and it was he who was "left one million dollars" in Harlow's will.

Harlow professed regret over "Dicky being drawn into this mess." A picture of Dicky was discovered among the defendant's effects and held for safekeeping in the office of the Department of Correction.

The defendant described his first meeting with Dennis Wepman, the accessory, as purely accidental and insisted that their relationship was platonic and based upon mutual intellectual interests. "He was one of the few I could relate to." Both were steadfast in their denials of any overt homosexual practices between them.

I first observed the defendant on the ward when he was unaware that he was being scrutinized. While he occasionally engaged in games and conversation with the other inmates, he displayed an unmistakable air of aloofness and condescension toward them, suggesting the feeling of grandiosity which later became readily demonstrable.

In initial interviews, it became evident that he was preoccupied excessively with those Greek legends and Shakespearean plays dealing predominantly with tragedy. Time and again, and spontaneously, he alluded to Greek characters out of Homer's *Iliad.* One of the principal gods mentioned was Aeneas, allegedly the offspring of Anchises, Prince of Troy, and of the goddess, Venus. But Harlow was suspiciously defensive in his vigorous denial of identifying himself with Aeneas or any other god. He said "Get this straight. I have no delusions. If I identified myself with anyone, it would be with Hamlet and his vacillations."

Toward the hospital routine, his attitude was supercilious and denunciatory. He even objected to being shaved by one of the personnel on the grounds that "it is an ignominious process to me, who has always had my own barber." Though generally unkempt, he donned the homely hospital robe in the manner of a Roman senator —as a toga thrown over his shoulders and tied at the neck.

In later conversations, he switched from Aeneas to Orestes, who was the son of Agamemnon, and the brother of Electra. According to the legend, "He was fated to kill his mother in order to avenge his father's murder of Clytemnestra and her lover, Aegisthus."

The defendant finally admitted a feeling of "sameness" with Orestes and the other gods. At this point it became even more evident to the examiners that we were confronted with something more serious than the flamboyant pretensions of an overt homosexual pseudo-intellectual. He really believed that he was superior to the rest of humanity, despite his record of inertia, fantasy, and non-accomplishment.

The question of feigning insanity in order to cover up a murder for material gain was carefully considered, but ruled out. The monies he had received previously were handled carelessly, if not haphazardly. His conscious thinking was so dominated by fantasy as to render him impervious to serious concern regarding financial matters. In his grandiosity, he conceived himself as a super being, transcending all mundane pursuits, which he regarded not only as idiotic but loathsome. Though he spoke of investments to a paternal cousin, he never actually made any. Neither did he show any inclination to work. Sneeringly, he asked "Why should I? Money never interested me. I always had it." (This was true.) His parents were known to have given him as much as 2 or 3 thousand dollars at a time.) Yet he requited this generosity with scorn and contempt. He alluded to any person who followed a gainful occupation as an imbecile.

That he was not simulating a psychosis became certain in later interviews with him during which he made the following comments: "You speak about the norm. In my case it is something that passes the normal and the abnormal.

"The weak have always banded together to destroy the strong. I'll be judged by men who are my peers. Hence I can't be judged to my own satisfaction.

"Mt. Olympus is a lonely place. So few of us are there. One wearies of continual hatred and contempt. My own idea of superiority may yet destroy me."

Regarding the crime, he mused. "It's so strange that I was not detected. I made many arch remarks which could be construed as complicity. It was a delightful game."

When questioned further apropos the tragedy, he described his father as having "the strength of ten because his heart was pure."

He was then asked to evaluate his actions in the light of the accepted codes incorporated in our normal framework of thinking and acting. He replied "Normal means usual or proper. In any case, as to my identity, it is something that surpasses normal and abnormal."

Alluding to his homosexual preoccupations, he stated:

"It is like a vastness for one who is three generations from the primordial ooze. "He (Dicky, the paramour) was a very talented young man—that is sexually." As to his involvement with his accomplice, he stated: "He was a perfect front for me. I knew that he was so stupid that he would give the whole thing away." Though he professed to feel vastly improved since becoming "gay," he still felt that "I was gradually destroyed from the outside world. I couldn't stand the laughter. People never understood me. I want the state to burn me and I'll see that it does. I always wanted people to like me, but they never did. I must succeed in making the jury hate me. The good die more blameless deaths. The men who live to bury them will have been clever enough to stay alive. I shall not die an ignominious death. I wish to die the proper way. There was a time when Seneca time and again opened a vein at dinner as Knebleo had put the curse on him, and he finally died. His was not an ignoble death. Just for doing this in society is no proof of it."

This type of equivocal thinking is one of the cardinal symptoms of schizophrenia, one cannot well relate it to present-day reality conceptions. The same holds true in regard to the defendant's grandiose delusions and identifications. These manifestations, together with the absence of appropriate affective responsiveness, spell a definite splitting in thought processes and emotions between reality and fantasy. They rendered Fraden exculpable from criminal responsibility.

At the formal hearing ordered by the Court, the following were present: Dr. Theodore S. Weiss and I, the examiners; Mr. James D. C. Murray, chief counsel for the defense; Mr. Alexander Herman, Assistant District Attorney in charge of Homicide; Dr. S. Bernard Wortis, Professor of Psychiatry at New York University and Dr. Morris Herman, his assistant professor. In addition, several witnesses such as relatives and the arresting officer were called to testify. None of those present attempted to controvert the findings of the examiners. Harlow Fraden was committed to Matteawan State Hospital.

Strange as it may seem, the co-defendant was found sane and capable of standing trial.

Dennis Wepman was born in Chicago in 1933, the younger of two siblings. According to the father, an attorney in Florida, the family setup was comparatively free from any major friction.

When he (the son) was 5 years old, we moved to Florida. There he completed grammar and high school without failure. However, he was never interested in school except for a few subjects such as literature and the drama. He was active in the school dramatic activities, clubs, etc., but never in sports. In high school he began to stay out late, 2-3 A.M. *His mother and I never had to disapprove of his friends (male) because they were usually older, sometimes considerably so. They were intellectuals and apparently admired his unusually good speech. He had developed this faculty spontaneously. His brother never had it and his mother and I had nothing to do with it. He always spoke of wanting to be* an actor, and expressed desires of attending college in the North. Being an alumnus of Michigan, I later arranged for his admission there. He always wanted to dominate any company he was in through his verbal ability. In this, as well as other interests he was in diametric opposition to his brother. He took offense when we attempted to advise or supervise him. He left the University of Michigan after one term, complaining that the schedules were too rigid. It was also learned that his time was occupied with the school paper and radio activities. We also heard that he had been suspected of involvement with homosexuals. Upon his return home, we sent him to a lay analyst, which arrangement was terminated abruptly by his departure for New York. Having many friends there, I found him work, but after a few months he quit because of no advancement. We felt hopeless because of his refusal to come home and discuss his plans. We didn't know anything about the crime until we saw an account of it in the newspapers.

A report from the Chief of Police of Ann Arbor, Michigan, revealed the following information:

He (the co-defendant) attended the University of Michigan from September 1950 to June 1951. He was requested to leave school because of his poor academic performance and the school's skepticism regarding his activities. There was doubt of his character because of his affiliation with known homosexuals, although there was never an admission by him that he was one.

In May of 1951 this Department arrested and tried

two University students charged with breaking and entering. These two students were known homosexuals. In May of 1951 he testified as an alibi witness in defense of one of these defendants. In his testimony he stated that he did not feel that the Kinsey Report had done justice to homosexuals in that it did not give them a fair chance. He denied that he was a homosexual himself, although he mingled with them freely for purposes of research. The reason he gave was that he was writing a book on the subject. His character was attacked at the trial, and the prosecution as well as myself felt that he possibly committed perjury.

His own version of his family and background was that it was "a run-of-the-mill family life." But he described "a rift," the development of an intense dislike between himself and his brother. The latter was extroverted, and popular and, as a consequence eulogized by their mother. Dennis became acutely aware of his inability to compete with his brother at the reality level. From then on, he assumed the role of scholar and man of letters. For a while, he subsisted upon his meagre earnings working for a publishing outfit called "Pocketbook." It was then that he was introduced into the elite "Bohemian set" in New York. There he continued his homosexual practices and relationships. He insisted that his "heart wasn't in it." He stated further, "I merely participated to meet celebrities. I even associated with a group of sado-masochists. I praticed flagellation merely as a sop to the crowd."

About a year prior to the double murder, he met the son of the deceased couple, more or less accidentally. He described his relationship with his co-defendant as an intellectual one. He said, "We talked about Greek legends, the philosophy of Nietzsche, and Elizabethan poetry." This is readily conceivable in the light of what has been brought out regarding the mental machinations of the other defendant. Both of the accused denied, and consistently so, that there had been any overt sexual practices between them. There was no reason to doubt this denial since the two had freely admitted previous homosexual activities with others.

At Bellevue, Dennis was at all times observed as cooperative and agreeable, quite a departure from the condescension and hauteur manifested by his accomplice. He was exceptionally articulate, displaying a superior vocabulary, though he sometimes used words incorrectly. He was genial and friendly, relating well to those about him. No delusional ideation or hallucinatory manifestations were noted at any time.

When the subject of his literary discussions with the co-defendant was broached, the superficiality of his thinking became obvious. He stated "We were both interested in poetry and literature." Regarding the Greek legends, he asserted that he was interested because "it was used as a process. The fact that there was an air of the grandiose intrigued me. We both loved Poe and Baudelaire, and other such diabolical writers." When questioned about his feelings at the time of the crime, he said, "It was an admixture of revulsion and curiosity—my impulse was not to run but to watch. I viewed the matter dispassionately. I thought of physiological reactions. They were merely hypothetical characters in our drama. I felt like a playwright viewing his play when it was first produced."

Asked whether he had had no sympathy for the victims, he replied, "Frankly, no. I didn't think of them as human beings. It would be the same if I watched the assassination of a president. I was fascinated by the grotesque, the fruition of weeks of planning. I never felt grief at the personal level." Unquestionably, he identified himself with the ruthless, maniacal accomplice through whom he attempted to bolster his own faltering ego inadequacy. In a rather smug, aloof, manner he stated, regarding the codefendant and aggressor, "I always felt like his analyst. I watched his consuming hatred of his mother reach the boiling point. I could not resist a comparison with the assassin in Poe's "The Cask of Amontillado." In that tale, the perpetrator had wreaked revenge upon an erstwhile friend and betrayer by entombing him through trickery. Dennis evidently perceived his grandiose and delusional confederate as a personage possessed of wealth and great erudition. Riding high with him, he, too, might become one of the great literati!

He described himself as "enthralled" by the overwhelming desire on the part of his accessory to destroy his parents. He stated that at first he was hesitant about participating in the crime because "it was too dangerous;" and further, that "the use of poison could arouse agonizing cries and capture." Later, he was convinced by his partner that the plan was so well organized as to prevent detection, and Wepman went on to say, "By observing it, I might further my literary ambitions."

So the situation resolved itself—Defendant #1 used defendant #2 as a stooge or foil. The latter was flattered by the selection of him as an accomplice in a theoretically insoluble crime. Even after his arrest and confession, he appeared to bask in the glory of it all. Actually, he had had no part in the premeditation, was not even acquainted with the deceased couple.

Our chief psychologist reported that Dennis Wepman scored a superior quotient of 123 on the intelligence test. Dr. David Wechsler, the author of the internationally used system of psychological scoring, reported:

His thinking is uneven, showing a marked difference between his abstract and concrete abilities. He is extremely pretentious, tends to set himself above other people, and generally overestimates his own capacity. The psychometric pattern, while resembling that of the schizophrenic co-defendant, shows less breaks in reality and an excessive narcissistic overestimation. On the personality side, he presents the picture of a severe character disorder. Along with an underdeveloped superego, he shows an impoverished emotionality and an inability to relate effectively to people. The tests further reveal a strong homosexual trend in which one may expect him to take the active role. They also show a basic aggressivity under a passive facade and a susceptibility to impulsive behavior.

In other words, we were dealing here with a person, who, though articulate, had lost his moorings regarding practical reality to the extent of being dominated by a psychotic individual whom he did not realize to be so. From a psychological point of view, he was *not* powerless to resist the temptation to participate in the patricide-matricide.

The son of the deceased, however, was suffering from a more serious mental disorder. His perceptions were dominated by delusional ideation. Such a condition prevented him from evaluating the responsibility of his performance.

Dennis was considered sane enough to suffer the penalty of his actions. He was sentenced to life imprisonment in a state prison.

14

Juveniles plot it coldly

A break in the plaster of paris murder of Mrs. Anna Gresh, 43, Eastside mother who was stabbed 21 times, appeared a possibility last night as police questioned her 15-year-old daughter, Theresa, for more than 11 hours.

JOURNAL-AMERICAN, 3/28/54

IN THIS CASE, too, the story of a "15-year-old peroxide blonde," as the press described her, and of her 17-year-old boy friend, who killed her mother, the relationship is a complementary one. The girl was the guileless dupe of the more aggressive male co-defendant. He thrived on her hero-worship and on her starry-eyed amazement of his ruthless actions.

The body of the mother was found in the bathtub of her apartment in mid-town Manhattan where, it was later ascertained, the boy had placed it, while the girl watched. The girl continued, off and on, to live in the apartment. When the smell became offensive, she and her boy friend sealed the body in 10 pounds of plaster of paris.

What goes on in the minds of the perpetrators of such an almost inconceivably hideous crime?

Well, what goes on in all our minds?

The average human being, starting his individual existence, is vaguely aware of an ego, a consciousness of self related to the people and the things that are about. As infants, we love or hate according to the affection or frustration we encounter. As we begin to grow, our reactions are conditioned by three major forces: the ego, the tempter, and the censor. The ego is the self. The tempter is the instinct, which knows no "right or wrong" while it is bent on satisfying the ego demands. The censor is the conscience, alerted through society's codes, which acts as a signal, warning us not to yield to the tempter—or we (the ego) will be ostracized socially or condemned criminally or both. A so-called normal ego usually conforms to the dictates of the censor. Fear of the ruling social censorship or of punitive measures is ordinarily powerful enough to act as a control.

But the not so normal ego rebels, consciously or unconsciously. In the case of the sociopath, the resistance is conscious and undisguised. A sociopath scoffs at censorship. His twisted self-confidence assures him that he can "master mind" society's moralists. The neurotic feels similar resistances to conformity. He does not indulge in any overt anti-social acts, however. His methods are the compulsions, the obsessions, the phobias, in other words the eccentricities which are his disguised expression of rebellion. Unconsciously, the neurotic has sought and found a circuitous method which enables him to resist and yet, at the same time, to escape detection or punishment. It is his negatively sublimated victory over the tempter. The psychotic, as shown in the cases already described, is never endowed with sufficient reality contact to enable him to be cognizant of either the tempter or the censor; hence the irresponsible and ruthless actions stemming from his fantasies—delusions and/or hallucinations.

Actually, there are many criminals who are neither

psychotic nor neurotic and not even classically sociopathic (those attempting to satisfy the ego, irrespective of consequences to themselves or to others). They are individuals enmeshed in social and economic confusions and frustrations from which the only escape seems to be the gang activity. In part, this explains the 'teen age gang organizations, the adolescent users of heroin, marijuana, cocaine, etc., and the muggers. Even the more serious crimes, the rapes, robberies, and murders, perpetrated by such individuals, though they are committed singly, tend to become epidemic, to go through a concatination or chain reaction. Most of these crimes appear weakly motivated. They seem to indicate an over-all defiance against any societal curbs rather than any personal animosity. Generally, we call these criminals cultural deviates. The "bathtub" matricide seems to belong in this category.

The Medical Examiner estimated that Mrs. Gresh had been dead from two to three weeks when the body was discovered. Numerous stab wounds gave mute evidence of the cause of death. At the time, the police could find no clue as to who the assassin or assassins were. Later they learned that a daughter was living with the mother of a boy friend who had just enlisted in the Marines. The boy's mother as well as the girl's maternal aunt were under the impression that Mrs. Gresh was in Florida. Theresa, the girl, had told them so.

This was an excellent lead. Others followed. In a very short time, Theresa and her Marine boy friend were taken into custody and charged with first degree murder. Both were committed to Bellevue.

The girl arrived at Bellevue first. Beyers, the boy friend, had to go through the preliminaries of release from the Marines. The examination of Theresa was begun.

A report from the Bureau of Attendance indicated that she had functioned satisfactorily in school. She was described as a "good student with good reports on behavior and work." She was also regarded as a "conforming, well-spoken and well-behaved child."

On the other hand, Mrs. Beyers, the mother of the co-defendant, described her as "unreliable in her statements and careless in her personal habits." Yet she, Mrs. Beyers, had assumed custody of the girl while her own mother "was away." It is possibly of some significance that the mother made these derogatory statements only after her son had been implicated.

Apparently, the early years of the girl were not happy ones. This may have been due to the fact that she never knew her father, and harbored doubts as to her legitimacy. Her confusion was further accentuated when her mother quarrelled and separated from him just two years prior to the tragedy. Obviously, the child's life had been a rather lonely one. She had never established any friendships, either with girls or boys. From what could be learned, it seems that Billy, the boy friend, was the first person to whom she had been able to relate. He was aggressive, physically prepossessing, and self-assured. That he displayed a particular interest in her was flattering. And when he continued his blandishments to the point of mentioning marriage, she was overcome to a state of unreasoning acquiescence to his every wish. She submitted herself with reckless abandon. As the District Attorney saw it, Dr. Cusack, the girl's defense psychiatrist was trying to present her as a Trilby in the clutches of a Svengali. The analogy did not seem to me very far-fetched.

The mother of the male co-defendant stated that she was under the impression that the deceased was a rather promiscuous woman. All of the witnesses we interviewed tended to corroborate this statement. The daughter was also cognizant of the facts. She related that on more than one occasion she had fortuitously run into her mother and paramours in compromising bedroom scenes. This came about because the mother worked on her job at night and carried on her liaisons while the daughter was at school. If the girl felt any resentment over this immoral behavior, I could not detect it. She seemed to accept it as a matter of course.

As to her own life, she mentioned being very lonely, having neither girl nor boy friends. She attributed her being "out of things" to the fact that she was overweight. Very wistfully, she told that the fellows never attempted to "date" her. They evidently regarded her as a lummox. Then, when Billy came along, expressing his affection for her, she succumbed to his desires apparently on a basis of unconditional surrender. She freely admitted that they carried on daily sexual orgies up until and even after the crime.

In discussing the offense, she was defensive and contradictory. This was quite understandable, considering the fact that she realized she was fighting for her life. She did, however, admit participation and complicity.

No evidence of any major mental disturbance was found. The following quotation is from the psychiatric report to the Court:

During her residence here (in Bellevue) she has at all times been cooperative, mingling freely with those about her and conversing freely and rationally with them. She likewise discusses her past life, schooling, etc., in a lucid manner. She has shown no particular emotional disturbance except upon her return from Court following indictment. Then she appeared depressed and was tearful, but only momentarily so. Subsequently, she has shown no sign of deep-seated, pathological depression. She described visions of her mother, on occasions at night, but when questioned more carefully about these experiences, she admitted that they actually occurred during a dream or a half-waking state. These phenomena were not regarded as being of a schizophrenic variety, inasmuch as she displayed insight into the unreality of the visions. At no time could any delusional trends be demonstrated. She disclaims ever having been persecuted by others. The closest she came to this was in her account of other girls at the school tending to ignore and ridicule her. She attributed this attitude to envy of her superior scholarship and good school adjustment.

From a psychiatric point of view, at no time were there any psychotic reactions observed. It was noted, however, that she is very suggestible and immature, sus-

ceptible to influences brought to bear by stronger, more aggressive individuals.

Our diagnostic impression is that we are dealing with a personality pattern disturbance of the schizoid type, without psychosis.

The special psychological testing revealed that she is of average intelligence, scoring an I. Q. of 98 on the Bellevue-Wechsler scale.

The general physical examination was essentially negative. She has, however, a juvenile acne of the face, as well as an acniform lesion of the scalp.

While upon admission she feared that she was pregnant because of a delayed menstrual period, all gynecological tests, including the Anheim-Zondeck proved negative.

The co-defendant, Billy, admitted readily that he was an accessory but insisted that the 15-year-old girl friend executed the stabbings and the bludgeonings. According to him, he merely aided the girl in concealing the remains in the bathtub, which included sealing the top of the vessel with plaster of paris. He made this statement, not knowing that a full copy of his confession to the District Attorney was already in my possession.

From the outset, it was evident that Billy Beyers was a "mama's boy." Like the girl, he had been the product of a broken home. Unlike her, however, he had been coddled and pampered. His mother had bolstered his ego with the idea that he was the "fair-haired boy" who could do no wrong. Thereby he developed a sense of ruthlessness regarding sexual conquests. He played the field at random.

In this affair, the female co-defendant had yielded readily to his caresses. But her mother had opposed matrimony. This was more than this fellow, the over-indulged one, could take. During this stage of frustration, the Tempter apparently said to the Ego (Self), "Who is this evil woman to interfere with a plan that I had conceived? My mother never did such a thing. How could this one dare?" It was at this point that he evidently decided to erase her.

In my personal interviews with him, I found him at all times arrogant with an assumed air of insouciance. He seemed to be saying: "Whatever happens, my mother will take care of me."

During his stay at the Hospital for approximately six weeks, he at no time evidenced even an inkling of psychotic thinking or behavior.

Our estimation of the case, from the psychiatric angle, which was submitted officially, read as follows:

He has been under constant observation since six weeks ago. During that interval, numerous examinations were conducted, but at no time was psychotic ideation, such as delusional trends or hallucinatory phenomena demonstrable. He consorted freely with the other inmates, indulging in their games, viewing television, etc. The past history as obtained from the mother, we do not regard as conclusive inasmuch as it was obviously biased. She painted an angelic picture of him, describing him as a model boy throughout his childhood. Yet we learn from him, as well as from other sources, that he had been consorting with unsavory neighborhood groups of delinquents whose company he sought voluntarily. This is further borne out by the information that we received that individuals of that ilk frequented the apartment of the deceased following the crime, indulging in revelry and drinking excesses. Our idea that the mother had been unduly protective of the defendant received further corroboration by her behavior at the Hospital. Despite the fact that she was advised by the Department of Correction regarding visits being allowed only by written permission from the office of the District Attorney, she became so vehement in her protests, as to become unmanageable. She was ultimately ejected.

As to the charge, the defendant has given several accounts, which are full of discrepancies and, likewise, do not coincide with the information we received from authentic official sources including a verbatim confession by him. His account of the relationship between his codefendant and himself, was manifestly unconvincing. For example, upon initial interview, he proclaimed his affection for the female accessory, and stated that he had planned to marry her because of her suspected pregnancy. The consummation of the act was to be in the form of an elopement. Yet, almost within the same breath, he recounted conversations with his mother in which he advised her to contact his girl friend, referring to another girl with whom he had associated prior to meeting the co-defendant. This sort of behavior, under such circum-

stances, further supported the opinion that the fickleness, vacillation and attitude of irresponsibility stemmed from an unreasoning overindulgence on the part of the mother.

These traits, in addition to his obvious egocentricity, strongly suggest a severe personality pattern disturbance. However, as was stated above, no psychotic ideation was at any time in evidence.

Ordinarily, the findings of the Psychiatric Court Commission are accepted without controversy. In this case, however, the mother of the male defendant attempted to disprove our contention that her son was sane and responsible for his murderous act. She did so, acting under her constitutional right. She retained a defense psychiatrist to controvert our evaluations. This move necessitated the selection of a jury of laymen to decide which was correct—the Court Commission, appointed on scientific merit and without compensation, or the psychiatrist retained personally by the mother. His testimony, as well as that of another psychiatrist, in behalf of the female defendant, is quoted below under the heading, "Excerpts from the Minutes of the Trial." My testimony is also quoted.

In his opening, the District Attorney, Mr. Vincent Dermody, encompassed the facts of the crime in such a manner, that no attempt was made on the part of either the defense counsel or the accused to refute them. The one question was which defendant was responsible for the stabbing and bludgeoning. Both admitted complicity, but each pointed the finger at the other in reference to the death-dealing blows. While there was obvious duplicity on the part of one or both of the defendants, neither manifested any sign of being confused or overpowered by any psychotic reactions, such as delusions or hallucinations. The psychiatrist retained in behalf of the male defendant appeared to imply that the latter was not in clear touch with reality and was in sort of trance at the time of the commission of the crime. The expert appearing for the girl, contended that she was coerced into participation and was powerless to resist the domineering influence of the male co-defendant. He did not maintain that she was psychotic.

Excerpts from the Minutes of the Trial

Mr. Dermody:

The defendants on or about the 4th of March willfully, feloniously and with malice aforethought struck and killed the decedent with a hammer and a knife . . . the evidence will show that within a few days after the first meeting of these defendants they became sexually intimate with each other, and that this sexual intimacy continued daily thereafter, generally taking place in the apartment of the girl while her mother was at work. It will further show that towards the end of the month (the one prior to the commission of the crime), *these two defendants decided that they wanted to get married; that she approached her mother and told her about the desire she had to marry the co-defendant. The deceased objected to any proposed marriage because of their youth. . . . It will further show that when the mother's objection was made known to the boy by the girl, they started to discuss the possibility of doing away with or killing the mother and taking over the apartment so that they could get married and live there. The first day of the month prior to the tragedy (which occurred on the 4th) they discussed ways and means of killing the mother. It will further show that on several occasions they discussed the possibility of turning on the gas and asphyxiating her. They also discussed the possibility of using some kind of poison. This was abandoned . . . as was the use of chloroform. Sometime in the morning or early afternoon of the killing . . . they agreed that it would be done by means of a hammer. The evidence will show that both these defendants knew what time the mother would return from work and the plan agreed upon by both of them was as follows: That she would wait in her bedroom at the appointed time when her mother was expected home; that she would remain there with radio turned up loudly; the co-defendant was to remain in the kitchen with the lights turned out, with the hammer, and that when the mother came in, he was to strike her over the head and kill her. The People expect to prove that from the statements of both these defendants, that at about ten P.M., according to plan, he left the bedroom where the girl was with the radio turned up loudly, walked into the kitchen, turned off the light, armed himself with a claw hammer and when she (the victim), came into the apartment, he struck her from behind several times with the hammer; over the head; then that he went into the bedroom where the co-defendant was waiting and told her that he had done it; that he then heard a noise in the kitchen and he saw the now deceased on her feet staggering to the hallway to get out of the apartment. The People then expect to prove that he grabbed her and that during the ensuing struggle, he dropped the hammer on the kitchen floor . . . that he knocked her down to the floor and held her down while she was struggling for her life, when he then called the co-defendant and asked her to pick up the hammer and give it to him. She refused to pick it up because it had blood on it. The male defendant then said "Well, give me something"; and we expect to prove from the mouth of the female co-defendant herself, that she went to the kitchen table and took a large bread knife in her hand, walked over to the boy and handed it to him and said "Use this" and that he plunged the knife in her heart at least six times. The evidence will then show that he then dragged the body from the hallway into the kitchen; that he took off the porcelain cover which was covering the bath tub, laid it down and placed the body of the mother into the tub; and further, that he then mopped up the blood on the kitchen floor and in the hallway, using rags that they found in the apartment; that after that, the two defendants went to bed. On the following day, they left the apartment and went over to the home of the male defendant's mother and told her, according to a pre-arranged plan, that the deceased had left the day before for Florida, and had abandoned her daughter completely. The evidence will show that from that time on, the female defendant at times would sleep in her own apartment, and at others, in the one occupied by her boy friend's mother . . . and that the body remained in the tub those five intervening days and that both these defendants discussed ways and means of disposing of the body . . . dismembering it or using acid or lime. Both of these plans were abandoned. Then the male defendant obtained a large cardboard box, brought it to the apartment, then attempted to fit the body into the box. The operation was unsuccessful. Then he obtained a blanket and wrapped the body in it, replacing it in the tub. The People expect to prove that on that same day (5 days subsequent to the murder), these defendants purchased a ten-pound bag of plaster of paris; that the male defendant returned to the apartment and that he applied the plaster of paris to the body as it lay in the tub. By his own statement he did this for the purpose of sealing off any possible odor until such time as he could decide how to dispose of the body. In the meantime, the evidence will show that both these defendants . . . told their friends that they had been married and that they now lived in this apartment. Apparently in "celebration" of the event, they held beer parties while the body reposed in the tub. The evidence will further show that sometime during the month in which the murder was committed, the male defendant enlisted in the Marines and that he left New York on a visit for a week, to his aunt in North Carolina, and upon his return he discovered that she, the co-defendant had been entertaining friends in the apartment during his absence and that he had an argument with her about this. In the mean-*

time, on the basis of the girl's claim that her mother had abandoned her without funds, she became a ward of the Children's Court (exactly 20 days after the crime and 2 days before the discovery of the body).

And, gentlemen, (the jury), *that was the situation. He was down in South Carolina in recruit training and she a ward of the Children's Court when* (22 days after the murder), *the superintendent of the apartment house, while sweeping the halls, detected a very strong and disagreeable odor coming from one of the apartments on the floor where the girl and her mother had resided.* (The unmistakable stench emanating through the keyhole of the door of this particular dwelling led to his contacting the police, inasmuch as he had no pass key . . .) *They made a search of the apartment and eventually lifted the lid off the tub, where they saw this mass of hard plaster of paris there. The evidence will show that the super got a stick and hit it from top to bottom of the plaster of paris, until he reached the bottom and as it broke a woman's stockinged foot came into view; and that the Medical Examiner, Dr. Benjamin Vance . . . found several lacerations of the scalp, and that the body showed twenty-one stab wounds, six of which penetrated the heart and mangled it, and he will testify that in his opinion the cause of death was these stab wounds which he found on the body.* (This he did, and in detail.) *There are other details involved. You will hear the testimony as to how, when this female defendant was first questioned, she told the story of the alleged abandonment by her mother and indicated to the detective that her mother was a woman of loose morals, that she was in the habit of having men in the apartment and that most likely one of her mother's boy friends had caused her death.*

You will hear finally from the testimony of a detective, how this defendant finally told him the story in which she admitted the plan of the killing, but insisted that the co-defendant did it.

The evidence will further show that upon this evidence detectives went to Parris Island, where they questioned the male defendant. At first he denied any knowledge of the death of the decedent. . . . When confronted, however, with the story that his girl friend had given the detectives, he then admitted that he had killed her mother, but at the time he claimed that the killing had been done as a result of him and the co-defendant having been found in a compromising position in bed by the mother. . . . The male co-defendant later changed his story and admitted that the killing was a planned one.

Mr. J. Michael Solomon, the defense counsel representing the male co-defendant, in his opening, made the following statements in his presentation:

We will show you that he, a 17-year-old boy in love, or supposedly in love, was in a state of mind that exists between a 15-year-old girl at the time when he got to know her, and he himself was not a most stable individual. I believe that it will become incumbent upon us as lawyers, and you, as jurors, to examine and bring out the state of mind that existed in this boy who is alleged to have plotted and planned a vicious, horrible murder, and show you, antecedent to the alleged crime, he had just made application for entry into the Marines. . . . As was necessary for his entry, he had to produce records of birth, and he discovered to his shocked amazement and what must have been a terrible blow to his youthful ego, that he was a bastard, that he was an illegitimate child mothered by his mother and a father he didn't know. But now with this knowledge and with the shock to himself—and let me say we may be able to produce for your proof by competent psychiatrists that even though he is suffering from psychotic or personality defects, was possibly sane enough to be tried, and sane enough to die for his crime if you so see fit . . . he, the defendant, will tell you that his statements of planning and those regarding his methods—gas chloroform and poisons—were the braggadocio of a stupid and emotionally disturbed youngster; that the mother was killed as a result of, or in the heat of, a passionate argument or fight with her own daughter. . . . The boy came in after, and though he may have participated in the gruesome and horrible acts, we will show you that under no consideration can they be charged to him as proof of his having been the person who planned and schemed and plotted the murder. We will show, I believe by competent proof, that he at the time was emotionally disturbed . . . that the mere facts of his existence at the time, which I think will make a question for you which you will have to decide, as to his sanity or lack of sanity at the time.

Both defendants were put on the stand. The testimony of neither negated their previous admissions of complicity. Yet, as I have mentioned before, each accused the other of conceiving, planning, and actually committing the heinous act. And again, in observing their behavior and in listening to their verbal responses, I could detect no sign of mental aberration or emotional disturbance.

The defendants had been under constant surveillance for weeks. They had been examined repeatedly by competent psychiatrists. Throughout their hospital residence, no protestations were registered regarding mental incapacity. All our painstaking efforts to seek out any signs of psychotic performance or thinking, prior to the murder, or to observe any mental aberrations, afterwards, proved fruitless. Yet, the mother of the male defendant, understandably distraught about her son, demanded that the Court allow the retention of an outside psychiatrist to controvert our conclusion as to his ability to make a defense for himself, the expenses to be defrayed by the State. Under the circumstances, a judge had no choice but to honor the request. In my opinion, however, the findings of the defense psychiatrists, both fully qualified physicians, were based primarily upon conjecture rather than demonstrable fact.

Abstracts of the psychiatric testimony from the minutes:

Dr. Charles Brown, for the male defendant. Direct examination.

Q. Have you made a psychiatric finding as to the defendant? A. Yes . . .

Q. Have you come to a conclusion as to whether the defendant was at the time laboring under such a defect of reason as not to know the nature and quality of his acts, or whether his acts were wrong? A. I have.

Q. And what is your conclusion? A. My conclusion is that the defendant was laboring under such a defect.

Q. From your examinations and study of the defendant based upon your experience, can you tell us whether there was a form of insanity this defendant was suffering from on the day of the crime? A. Yes. I feel that he was the victim of a psychotic reaction.

Q. Would you be able to classify the form of insanity he was suffering from at that time by any other terms? A. More specifically, chronic schizophrenia.

Q. Can you tell us upon what you base this finding, Doctor? A. My opinion is that what is important, particularly in a situation like this, is an evaluation of the total adjustment of the individual involved and an estimate of the total situation as it presents itself against the life pattern of the patient. Now in the present instance I feel that this total situation, in my opinion, is unnecessary, useless, purposeless, disgusting, degrading. That is the way I look at these facts that have transpired, beginning in (month of the killing), up to the present time. Now I would feel that an individual who becomes progressively involved in a situation that is useless, unnecessary, purposeless, disgusting and degrading, must be the *victim of a towering incompetence. Now I feel that that estimate applies to the defendant.*

Q. *Now if I were to tell you that it is claimed that you killed the deceased because she did not want you to marry her daughter, would you say that that is a fact that you took into consideration?* A. *It is.*

Q. *Dr. Brown, mindful of the chronology in this case, is it a fact that you saw and examined and interested yourself in this case antecedent to the time when he was examined by the doctors at Bellevue?* A. *Yes.*

Q. *Now it was after you had seen the defendant sometimes that a report was prepared by the psychiatrists at Bellevue Hospital; is that correct, sir?* A. *That is.*

Q. *And that is the report that you have on your lap now?* A. *That is correct.*

Q. *Now, do you find anything in that report to substantiate your position . . . ?* A. *I find that this is an excellent report and I agree with all the observations, except the final conclusion* (which stated that the defendant was not in such a state of insanity as to be incapable of understanding the charges against him or of making a defense thereto).

From the Cross-examination by Mr. Dermody, the Assistant District Attorney:

Q. *Doctor, if I understand your testimony correctly, you started to specialize in psychiatry about ten years ago?* A. *That is right.*

Q. *I believe you also said you did serve your internship at Bellevue Hospital?* A. *That is right.*

Q. *Was that at the Psychiatric Division?* A. *That is right.*

Q. *At that time do you recall having occasion to meet and know Dr. Cassity who sits at the People's counsel table?* A. *That is right.*

Q. *At the time was Dr. Cassity one of the Senior Psychiatrists there?* A. *He was.*

Q. *Now, you have testified that you have examined the report (from Bellevue) and you have read it to the jury?* A. *Yes, sir.*

Q. *And you indicated that in your opinion there were not enough details supplied in that report regarding the background, specifically the relationship between the defendant, the co-defendant and the deceased; am I correct in that, Doctor?* A. *That is one of the aspects; yes, sir.*

The D.A. then elicited from the doctor the admission that he had never seen or examined the defendant until about eleven weeks subsequent to the tragedy. The doctor still insisted, that in his opinion the accused was insane both at the time of the murder as well as at the time of his testimony. Though he had said little to convince one of this fact, I think that I know what he meant—which was, that the boy was warped emotionally from the beginning to such an extent as to paralyze his judgment. While I disagree completely with this opinion, I still believe a doctor should be afforded a chance to express a free opinion, unhampered by formal methods of cross-questioning such as appear below.

Q. *Now, Doctor, you testified that in your opinion . . . the defendant* (who was examined 11 weeks after the crime) *did not know the nature and quality of his acts at the time of the murder, or that he knew that it was wrong?* A. *Yes.*

Q. *Would you mind stating whether it is your opinion as to the present moment?* A. *Yes, it is.*

Q. *Now, Doctor, what do you understand by the meaning of the words "not to know the nature and quality of the act he was doing?"* A. *The nature of the act involves the manipulations, what he did; the quality involves the dangerousness of it, the general significance of it.*

The Court: The nature of the act, Doctor, would include whether or not he had a hammer or a knife in his hand. Would you say that on the day of the death of the deceased he did not know that he was holding a knife or a hammer? Witness: I am obliged to. (The D.A. objected to the answer in regard to the use of the word "obliged.")

The Court: Strike it out.

Considerable questioning followed along the same line, both by the Court and the District Attorney. The doctor stated that he thought the defendant was mentally ill and that he was suffering from a psychiatric disorder known as schizophrenia (a splitting in thinking and emotivity between reality and fantasy). I was in total disagreement with the doctor's evaluation. But, again, I do not feel that he had ample opportunity to support his conviction. From the little that he said or was allowed to say, there was virtually nothing to validate his diagnosis. What he meant to say, I believe, was that due to mental derangement, the defendant did not fully UNDERSTAND what he was doing. This distinction between knowing and understanding is one which the Courts have been prone to misconstrue, with resultant confusion in the minds of the witnesses. To know is merely to perceive, to recognize, to have cognizance of, but without implication of understanding. Many psychotic and mentally defective individuals know when they are in an institution, but they certainly do not *understand* the full significance of their position.

The next witness for the defendant, retained in behalf of the girl, was Dr. Thomas S. Cusack. He agreed that the defendant was sane (not psychotic) before, during, and after the participation in the crime. He qualified this statement of opinion, however, with the following rejoinder, in response to the question asked by the attorney retained by the female defendant.

From the Minutes:

Q. *Now, Doctor, what is your opinion as to whether she was able to think and reflect and make a volitional choice in the process of thinking and reflecting?* A. *In the first place, she was an immature, suggestible type, standing in the dawn of adolescence; she had not yet grown up, and she lived under very strange conditions. She had a very decided unhinging, morally. Her will power was afflicted. She was not a free agent. She did not have the power of choice to reflect and consider, and because of that she was inadequately unable to plan, design, contemplate, premeditate and form a judgment.*

Q. *And, Doctor, in your opinion, based upon the question and upon what you have observed in connection with statements, falsifications to various officers and others, would you have an opinion with respect to the ability and capacity to think and reflect and make a volitional choice with respect to these on the part of the defendant?* A. *That is a rather difficult question, but I'll say this, that these types follow the path of least resistance, lose a certain amount of their inhibitions and will say anything, either for good or bad. Sometimes they develop what I would say is this—it's two big words, but I'll explain them:*

Pseudologia phantastica—that's fantastic, false statements as self-deserving declarations, either to aid them or what; but they do lose the power of inhibitions and are suggestible. They think the answer they give is what the person who is interrogating them wants.

Under cross-examination, the doctor held tenaciously to his contention that "she was not a free agent" and that she did not have the power of choice.

As to the psychopathological disease entity, pseudologia phantastica—I described its history and clinical manifestations before the New York Society of Clinical Psychiatry about three years ago, under the title of "The Psychodynamics of Pseudologia Phantastica." The symptoms usually begin in childhood, and are characterized by the patient's representing himself or herself, as emanating from royal parentage, having access to large amounts of money, or of possessing a secret entree to an elite coterie of socialites. Nothing in this defendant's history, as obtained from her aunt or from the school authorities, suggested any such ideation. Nor could I detect even an inkling of it in any of my personal interviews. Similarly, the descriptive phrases used by the doctor, seemed to me to have no validity in a murder case; they are too vague, non-descriptive, inconclusive. One could allude to almost any young person in the following terms without making out a case of irresponsibility: 1) She was immature, suggestible and standing in the dawn of adolescence; 2) She was not a free agent. (An insinuation that she had a hand in the murder because of the fear of her boy friend;) 3) Inability to select choice of action.

When I was called to the stand, I naturally anticipated a rigorous effort to controvert my written opinion that neither of the defendants was insane or psychotic, either before or at the time of the execution of the crime. Much to my surprise, no such approach materialized. What did become immediately evident was: 1) The District Attorney was disposed to charge complete culpability and complicity on the part of both defendants. 2) The defense attorneys for both the male and female defendants were in a constant hassle as to whether the girl had been in the throes of an epileptic furor (state of organic confusion and excitement) or had been beset by a reactive state of depression when taken to the precinct following the murder, giving rise to an overwhelming fear of the co-defendant's threats and propelling her into a confession. 3) Mr. Solomon, counsel for the female co-defendant, strove to discredit my testimony upon the grounds of epilepsy.

My conclusions, however, remained the same:

1. I saw no evidence of schizophrenia or any other psychotic state in the male defendant.

2. The same held true for the female co-defendant.

3. At no time did the female culprit manifest any signs of an organic nature, such as epilepsy.

4. Neither defendant, during the fairly protracted stay in the Hospital, displayed any ostensible symptoms of emotional instability.

The boy was convicted and sent to the electric chair.

The girl was convicted of 2nd degree murder and sentenced to prison from twenty years to life.

15

A hatchet and a trauma

A pretty 16-year-old Queens school girl stood on the line-up platform at Police Headquarters yesterday morning, charged with the hatchet-slaying of a 71-year-old tailor from whom she had stolen $5 after the killing.

NEW YORK TIMES, 10/22/45

THE THREE CASES I am now about to discuss had one factor in common. Each murderer had, at some time in his or her life, suffered a trauma which, in turn, had produced a brain change.

The post-traumatic brain syndrome or symptom chain is usually characterized by a state of confusion which may be periodic or chronic and may even take the form of a temporary amnesia, by varying degrees of excessive irritability, and finally, by episodes of emotional explosiveness that are closely akin to frenzy. The symptoms become noticeable almost immediately following the injury. In this sense, they are completely unlike the temper tantrums, amnesia-like truancies, and delusional thinking often attributed by the lay public to a head injury. Here, there is no definite time relationship to the alleged trauma. And the encephalographic tests, which show the rate of conduction of brain impulses, are usually negative. In cases of actual traumatic origin, the tests show abnormally accelerated activity.

The trauma symptomatology may often resemble the symptoms of epilepsy or of post-encephalitis. But here, too, the differences are readily recognizable. In epilepsy, the victim becomes emotionally torpid and sluggish after his convulsive seizure. In chronic encephalitis (infection of the coverings of the brain), the excitements and amnesias are strictly sporadic, and usually so mild as to escape attention. Also—encephalitis cases manifest a monotony in emotivity and stereotopy in thinking that is never observed in post-traumatic cases. A further dissimilarity is noted in the sexual behavior of the two. The post-traumatic patient rarely resorts to abnormal sex practices, whereas the post-encephalitic does so excessively, but only occasionally in a vicious way. As a rule, he indulges in peeping, touching, exhibitionism, and making suggestive approaches to minors.

The female, among the three post-traumatic brain syndrome cases which follow, suffered a head injury at the age of 8. She developed violent headaches which continued to occur periodically. According to her aunt, she began, too, to have fainting spells and memory blanks about recent happenings. Her behavior became irascible, impetuous, and erratic. Temper tantrums were frequent, nail-biting, chronic, and school attendance, sporadic. She pretended to be at school when she was actually spending her time at the beach.

Helena Theresa Nienstedt was 16 years old when she was picked up for murder. She had bludgeoned a tailor, a man in his early seventies, with a hammer. Her mother had been having illicit relations with this man.

Helena, or Lena as she was usually called, was born in Long Island, out of wedlock. The mother's history included a commitment from Bellevue to a state hospital because of schizophrenia. There was also a history of mental disorder among other maternal relatives. But the girl showed no noticeable signs of mental illness until the head injury, a result of a bus accident.

The mental aberrations of the mother may have had no apparent effects on the consciousness of the child. They may well have had an effect upon her unconscious thinking, though. Certainly, the promiscuity and the illicit relations with the tailor could scarcely have missed making some deleterious impression upon the defendant.

It seems highly doubtful, however, that the killing would have taken place if she had not suffered the organic brain damage. The mother's behavior merely triggered the murderous impulse, which was further propelled by her excessive drinking, a habit usually rare in adolescence.

Lena was sent by the Court to Bellevue Hospital for an appraisal of her mental responsibility. The admitting note, prepared and recorded by Dr. Graser, reads as follows:

Q. *Charge? Why arrested?* A. *Because I killed somebody, the tailor man.*

Q. *Why?* A. *I don't know why. I seem to have forgotten.*

Q. *Please try to explain?* A. *I know he tried to get fresh with me.*

Q. *How?* A. *He put his hand on my breast and I*

pushed him away. He went around by the sewing machine and I took out the hatchet and hit him; a good smack, too, poor thing.

Q. *Why have a hatchet?* A. *I always carry things like that; like yesterday, a girl was making a noise there and it bothered me and I choked her; it bothered me like a clock, clock, clock.*

Q. *How feel about the death of the old man?* A. *Well, I feel sorry for him, but I don't feel like I did it.*

Q. *How long did you know him?* A. *About three years; he was good to me and to everybody. He never harmed anybody.*

Q. *Harm you?* A. *No, the old man wouldn't harm anybody. He put both hands on my breasts, but I didn't hit him for that. I seemed to get some satisfaction when I hit him. A lot of fellows had been fresh with me before. After I had the bus accident at eight, I seem to forget things; like I'll read a story and a little while later somebody will ask me about it and I won't remember. Like I'll read a story and about 20 minutes later somebody will ask me about, and I won't remember so I don't read, it is a waste of time.*

Abnormalities in her thinking, feeling and acting, became apparent a day or two following her admission. I remember my initial interview with her:

She entered the office quietly and gave correct and coherent answers to questions regarding statistical data (age, birth, illnesses, habits, etc.). As our interrogations continued, however, she began to show signs of emotional tension, such as twitchings of the body, biting the lips and nails, and making facial grimaces. It was when she admitted the knowledge of her illegitimacy that she began to yell and scream and suddenly rushed from the office. She returned to the ward crying, but the nurses' notes indicate that a few moments later she was laughing and joking and playing cards with the other patients.

The following day she again became upset and exclaimed to a nurse, "My head is banging and I think I heard the words 'kill, kill, kill.' " Then, she said, "If I killed anyone else that would be only one more murder." Later, she was overheard remarking to another patient, "I have a force of some kind in my head like an urge. I had an urge to kill, so I hit the old man. When the blood splashed over my face, I liked the feeling of it." The nurses' notes continued, however, to describe her as quite cheerful, suggesting the completely transitory character of the murderous impulse.

A few days later I resumed my examination. The recorded excerpts follow:

Q. *What kind of place is this?* A. *Crazy house.*

Q. *Do you think that you belong here?* A. *Maybe I do. I forget where I put things. I get mixed up.*

Q. *How?* A. *I have a throbbing in the head and they go "Boom, zoom, zip." They go on anywhere from minutes to two or three days. I throw anything that I get hold of. I just sit and stare. I know where I am, but my mind goes blank.*

Lena Nienstedt was, as I have mentioned, 16 when I met her. Her hair was long, brown, and curly; her eyes, large and starry. Her figure was proportionately formed. Her facial expression was saucy and provocative. She was as beautiful as many a young actress. Yet she had few or scarcely any boy friends. Her poutiness, her petulance, her extreme impetuousness upon the slightest provocation probably made relationships difficult. These reactions were all part and parcel of her organic brain ailment.

Early one morning, I received an S.O.S. from the hospital nursing office, urgently requesting my presence in the Female Criminal Service. Upon arrival, I found Lena in her room. The bed coverings were strewn about the floor, her hair and clothes were dishevelled, and she obviously did not recognize me, though she had been seeing me daily for a week. I asked what was troubling her. She began to shout and to make menacing gestures. She screamed, "Who the hell are you? Get out of here, you bastard!" My efforts to conciliate her were useless. I ordered her sedated intramuscularly.

The next day she came into my office as though nothing had happened. She greeted me with a cheery "Hello, Doc, where have you been? I haven't seen you lately." We talked, this time, about the details of the crime. The following is her verbatim account:

I was on my way down town to the candy store to get a soda, when I noticed old J's door open. (He was the deceased tailor.) *I like old J, and I walked in. He said,*

"Hello, there, you sure look pretty this morning." Then he put his hands on my chest. (Did you think that he was attempting to get familiar?) *Who, old J.? He wouldn't harm a fly. But something came over me and I pulled my hatchet out of my bag and hit him on the head. He fell, and he was bleeding. He made awful gurgling noises and the blood splattered on my dress. I hit him again and those awful noises stopped.* (What did you do then?) *I went home and soaked my dress; otherwise it would be ruined. Then I went to bed.* (Did you sleep well?) *I read a detective story and then went to sleep. I never slept better in my life.* (Following day?) *The next morning I went down to the candy store. When I got there the fellow behind the counter said "Did you hear about the old man?"* I asked, *"What old man?" He said "Old J., the tailor got his brains knocked out." I started to laugh. He then said, "What's the matter with you, are you crazy?" I said "no, it just sort of struck me funny." I felt glad about going back the second time to get my hatchet; because if my mother had missed it, she would have raised hell."*

On the basis of the intermittent emotional explosions and the positive findings in the encephalographic readings, my report stated that the defendant was suffering from an organic brain disease and recommended commitment to the Matteawan State Hospital for the Criminally Insane. The recommendation was accepted.

But, 9 years later, I met Mr. James D. C. Murray, the distinguished trial lawyer, in the Supreme Court. He asked me whether I remembered the Nienstedt defendant, told me that, while interviewing one of his clients at Matteawan, his attention had been called to Lena. He had interviewed her at length, believed she was capable of standing trial, and had issued a writ of habeas corpus charging the state with the duty of showing reasons for further detention. The relatives, through Mr. Murray, retained Dr. Thomas Cusack to give an estimate of her mental capabilities in reference to standing trial. I was called, by subpoena, to demonstrate that she had shown signs of mental illness at the time I examined her.

Mr. Murray requested that I remain in court while the defendant was testifying in her own behalf. I listened to her testimony for over an hour. Unlike the many times that I had interviewed her at Bellevue, when she was distraught to the point of incoherence, she was, on the stand, completely complacent and coherent.

She did not seem at all concerned, now, either about her illegitimacy or her mother's illicit relationships. She accepted her out-of-wedlock birth as "one of those things." She affectionately called the tailor "Old J." and she spoke of him as "a good guy."

Still—she had not, until the murder, actually displayed any vindictiveness about him, either. Nor had she been overly disturbed by her mother's waywardness. Her condition was an organic one. Since the age of 8, when the trauma had occurred, she had been prone to violently opposing personality changes. Her drinking, too, was probably the result of the injury, the unconscious relief she sought for the brain irritation. I was not sure that her present calm indicated any significant change. I so testified at the hearing on the writ to show cause why she should not be released from custody.

The defendant was ordered back to Bellevue for reexamination. She was again interrogated extensively by Dr. Weiss and myself, as well as by other members of the staff, over the period of a month.

The following quotations are from the second report, which we subsequently submitted to the Court.

During her present residence here, she has been at all times alert and cooperative. She stated that she had only a faint recollection of her stay here 9 years previously and that she could recall having seen only one doctor, Dr. Grazer, the psychiatrist who admitted her. (This claim I am inclined to credit, inasmuch as she obviously did not recognize me in court at the time of the hearing. Mr. Murray was obliged to identify me.) She claimed further that her mind did not begin to clear until about the end of her second year in Matteawan. At the present time, her thinking is lucid, and her emotional responses were found to be appropriate. She likewise shows none of the physical signs of the organic brain syndrome, which we had observed previously; namely, facial twitches, head tremors, and constant nail biting. The encephalographic findings are now negative.

Despite the remission of the above mentioned symptoms, they were unquestionably of organic origin, and we warned in our report that a recurrence of them was conceivable. We consequently recommended that she be required to receive periodic psychiatric check-ups in the event of her release from custody.

The Court apparently concurred in our opinion that the defendant was not mentally responsible at the time of the crime. He paroled her in the care of Mr. Murray.

Three years have now elapsed, and as far as can be learned, there have been no repetitions of the psychotic episodes.

16

The injured brain is unhealed

Two Held in Killing. Hearing Is Set for September 6 in Shooting of Aged Jeweler. ...The suspects are....and Albert John De Cicco, 35, of 1518-86 Street, both in Brooklyn....De Cicco has a record of four gambling arrests, the police said.

NEW YORK TIMES, 8/29/55

THE PROBLEM of mental responsibility in defendants suffering from organic brain ailments needs, I believe, to be re-evaluated. In my opinion, people subject to epilepsy or like diseases and people with histories of severe head injuries can not be dismissed as irresponsible. It is only when a definite personality change has occurred as the result of a trauma or of a cerebro-spinal affliction that exculpability can be considered. In the "hatchet murder," there was definitely a change in the behavior pattern. The point is further demonstrated in the murder that follows:

Albert DeCicco, the defendant, was charged with having taken part in the hold-up murder of a jewelry establishment in downtown Manhattan. The proprietor was shot. There were two additional accomplices.

Neither the defendant's counsel, Mr. Maurice Edelbaum, nor the Assistant District Attorney, Mr. Robert Reynolds, could elicit any coherent responses from him after his arrest. Both reported that he seemed in a daze. At the request of his attorney and with the acquiescence of the District Attorney, DeCicco was committed to Bellevue for observation.

A day or two after the admission, Mr. Edelbaum telephoned me. He explained that he wanted to give me an important bit of information. It might be helpful in my evaluation of the case. He then advised me that he had previously represented the defendant in an accident action in New Jersey. He reported as follows:

In 1952, while working in the hold of a boat as a stevedore-carpenter, the winch went out of order, and he was struck on the head by a swinging pipe and knocked unconscious. Since then, for the past 4 years, he has been unable to work on account of severe headaches and memory lapses.

I examined DeCicco on several occasions. I also watched him on the ward daily. He was at all times seclusive, seemed detached and perplexed. He did not talk to or mingle with the other prisoners. He gave correct answers to questions about statistical data but professed a complete amnesia regarding the crime and regarding the head injury in 1952, as well. He did not seem to me to be dissimulating. It could scarcely have been to his advantage not to cooperate or to confer with his attorney about the accident suit, which was still pending. Not only that—he gave no sign of recognizing Mr. Edelbaum when the attorney visited him at the hospital. Though there were no indications of any hallucinations, the District Attorney agreed that an attempt to try DeCicco at this point would prove futile. The Court, therefore, ordered a formal hearing.

Present at the proceeding were Mr. Robert Reynolds, the Assistant District Attorney in the Homicide Division of the Prosecutor's office, Mr. Maurice Edelbaum, counsel for the defendant, and Dr. Theodore S. Weiss and I, the designated official examiners.

The first witness called was the wife of the defendant. She stated that she had known her husband since childhood. They were married when she was 16 and he 18. Their two male children were now 16 and 10. When questioned about his school and social adjustments, she replied that he was an average student, had many friends and was a "happy-go-lucky" type. She described their marriage prior to 1952 as a "normal" one. They had no serious quarrels and he was a good provider. He used neither alcohol nor drugs. At this point, I reminded her that she had told Dr. Weiss and me about certain changes in him following the accident, and requested that she repeat the historical account that she gave us for the benefit of the others present. Among the things that she mentioned in this regard were the following:

He began to keep to himself a lot, complained of headaches. He got dizzy spells going up a ladder and couldn't work any more. He got violent at me and threatened to hit me for no reason. One time he broke the furniture in his mother's house. (When his mind sort of went off, was this periodic and were there times when he was mentally clear?) *Yes, sometimes he would act like his old self.* (She was then asked about his attitude toward her during her visits to him at Bellevue.) *He doesn't talk too much. If I speak to him, he answers, sometimes he doesn't. I asked him if he saw a lawyer. He said he didn't know, but that some fellow visited him who said he was a lawyer.* (This was Mr. Edelbaum who had also represented him in the accident case.)

The defendant was then called into the hearing room. At first he was a bit tearful. Apparently, this was the result of his just having seen his wife in the corridor. He appeared puzzled and bewildered. I explained the purpose of the proceeding to him.

The quotations from the minutes will illustrate his responses:

Questioning by Dr. Cassity: Q. *How do you feel?* A. *All right.*

Q. *I know you are a little tearful. You saw your wife, that accounts for that. You probably know, or realize, this is just a hearing to see how your thoughts are operating at this time. You know this doctor (indicating Dr. Weiss)?* A. *I think so.*

Q. *What is his name?* A. Dr. Cassity or Dr. Weiss.

Q. *This is Dr. Weiss. Do you know this gentleman here* (indicating Mr. Edelbaum?) A. *He was here once.*

Mr. Edelbaum: *Do you know who I am?*

Witness: *Tell me your name.*

Q. *This gentleman here. Did you ever talk to him? His name is Mr. Reynolds. Do you remember him?* A. No.

Mr. Reynolds: *I was in the station house.*

Witness: *I don't remember you.*

Q. *Where were you born?* A. New York City.

Q. *How far did you go in school?* A. *High school.*

Q. *Did you graduate?* A. *I don't remember.*

Q. *What kind of work have you done most of your life?* A. *No answer.*

Q. *Did you understand the question?* A. *Yes. I don't remember.*

Q. *Do you remember getting injured?* A. *No. I don't know anything about that.*

Q. *Do you remember being hit while at work?* A. *No.*

Mr. Edelbaum: *He was hit with a steel pipe.*

Q. *Do you remember that—what Mr. Edelbaum said? You were struck with a steel pipe. Do you remember that?* A. *No.*

By Dr. Weiss: Q. *Do you remember being in a compensation action to get money for the accident?* A. *No sir.*

Q. *You don't remember anything about it?* A. *I don't know anything about it.*

By Dr. Cassity: Q. *In this proceeding here and our preceding examination we have been trying to determine whether you are capable of understanding the charges against you. Do you know what charges are against you?* A. *I know what I am told.*

Q. *What were you told?* A. *I was told I am on a homicide charge.*

Q. *Who did they say was killed?* A. *They didn't tell me.*

Q. *Do you remember being arrested?* A. *No sir.*

Q. *You don't remember talking to Mr. Reynolds, the District Attorney?* A. *I never seen him.*

Q. *What is today?* A. Thursday—Friday.

Q. *What month is this?* A. June.

Q. *How long have you been in this place here?* A. About 7 weeks.

Q. *What is the name of this place?* A. Bellevue Hospital.

Q. *What was the purpose of the Court sending you to Bellevue Hospital?* A. I don't know.

Q. *Have you any idea of the kind of cases there are in the ward with you, what type of cases?* A. I don't know what you mean.

Q. *Tuberculosis cases, or heart cases, or what are they?* A. I don't know what they have there.

By Dr. Weiss: Q. *On the ward are there bars?* A. Yes.

Q. *What does that mean?* A. Jail.

Q. *It is a jail. At the same time you realize it is Bellevue Hospital. No matter whether you are in the jail section or not, people are here for observation, for disease, and it is physical or mental. Do you think you are here for observation for physical or mental?* A. I don't know why I am here.

Q. *How are you treated here?* A. Nobody bothers me.

Q. *Do you eat regularly?* A. Yes.

Q. *Do you sleep well?* A. Not so good.

Q. *Would you prefer being in a prison or in a hospital?* A. I don't prefer any of them. I prefer to go where I belong, with my people.

Q. *How can you be with your people before this murder charge is disposed of?* A. I don't know anything about *this charge. They tell me about charges. I don't know nothing about the charge.*

Q. You don't remember going into detail with your counsel, Mr. Edelbaum, with regard to the accident? A. No.

Q. Do you know his name? I just told you. Do you know his first name? A. That is Edelbaum.

Q. What is his first name? A. *I know him as Mr. Edelbaum.*

Q. When was the last time you saw Mr. Edelbaum? A. *I saw him here.*

Q. What was the time before that that you saw him? A. *I don't remember ever seeing him.*

Q. In other words, you wouldn't know he was Mr. Edelbaum if we didn't identify him to you, is that right? A. That's right.

Q. What part of your head do you have the pain? Put your hand on the part of the head where you have the pain. A. *Most of the time I get a pain right around here.* (Indicating front part of the head.)

By Dr. Weiss: Q. Not in back? A. *It feels like it is all over.*

Q. Any trouble in your eyes? A. *When I get a pain they tear a lot.*

Q. Any other pains besides the head and eyes? A. You mean on my body?

Q. Anywhere on your body? A. That is all.

Q. Any dizziness? A. Once in a while.

By Dr. Cassity: Q. How do you think you got involved in a homicide: How do you think anybody suspected you were involved? A. That is something I can't seem to find out.

Q. You don't remember talking to Mr. Edelbaum about it? A. No.

By Dr. Weiss: Q. What did they tell you about the charge? A. I wasn't told that.

By Dr. Cassity: Q. Do you know a man named Goldberg? A. No.

By Dr. Weiss: Q. Did you know any Goldberg? A. No.

Q. Did you ever carry a weapon in your life, or own one, a gun? A. Own a gun?

Q. Yes. A. No sir.

Q. How do you feel towards us now, Dr. Cassity and myself? How do you feel towards us? Are we all right? A. Yes.

Q. Do we seem fair to you? A. Yes.

Q. Has anybody bothered you in the ward? A. No.

Q. They have been friendly? A. Yes.

Q. What have you done during the day? Did you sit around or mix? A. They made me help in the kitchen.

Q. Did you talk to the other prisoners? A. A word here and there.

By Dr. Cassity: Q. Do you remember the names of any of them? A. Yes.

Q. Name one or two? A. The one that sleeps next to me.

Q. What is his name? A. V——

Q. Do you know what V—— is charged with? A. No.

By Dr. Weiss: Q. How do you feel, happy, sad, you

don't care; you are disinterested? How do you feel, worried or what? A. *I don't feel right here. I don't belong here.*

Q. *Do you feel irritable about being here?* A. *I feel I don't belong here.*

Q. *There is a charge against you. What do you think is back of it?* A. *I don't know.*

Q. *How do you try to theorize about it?* A. *I can't explain it to myself.*

Q. *You must have some information. You think it is because your memory is poor?* A. *I don't know.*

Q. *Is your memory poor?* A. *I don't know if it is poor or not.*

Q. *This man tells you there is a compensation proceeding. If you don't know it, your memory is poor. What do you think about it? You have no explanation?* A. *I don't know.*

Dr. Cassity: *All right. That is all.*

(Witness excused—hearing ended)

Albert DeCicco was recommended for hospitalization. There would have been no point in attempting to try him on a murder charge at that time. This in no way, however, absolved him of guilt or complicity in the crime. If and when he recovered his mental faculties, he would still be held culpable for his involvement in the criminal act.

He was committed to Matteawan State Hospital for the Criminally Insane. During the first months of his stay there, he displayed virtually the same symptoms as those described. Later on in the year, however, he recovered his memory, recalling not only the head injury and compensation proceedings attendant thereon, but the role he played in the murder. He was returned to Bellevue for reappraisal.

Examination showed him to be in a state of complete remission (improvement) from his psychosis. He maintained that he had only a faint recollection of his previous stay in Bellevue. But he stated that he clearly remembered the head injury and the fact that he had been awarded $74 compensation on a bi-monthly basis. As to his being an accessory to the murder, he made the following admission:

My compensation had run out. I tried to go back to work, but couldn't make it on account of the headaches and "blackouts". I met my friend, X, and he asked me if I wanted to make a couple of dollars. Imagine asking me that in my down and out condition! He introduced me to a guy named "G". ("G" later admitted the shooting.) *The three of us went to a building and got off at the 7th floor, I believe. The other two guys walked into an office with a jewelry sign on the door. I knew it was a stickup, but I didn't know nothing about any gun. I was supposed to be the lookout. The next thing I knew, I heard a shot. We were caught in the building.*

From this statement, two facts became apparent: one, that he had definitely not been simulating during his previous admission at Bellevue; and two, that his episodic mental disturbances bore no relationship to the crime. Hence, despite the presence of an organic brain involvement, he was responsible as an accessory before the fact. He admitted as much and accepted his predicament philosophically.

With the consent of the District Attorney, the Court accepted a plea of murder in the second degree, which carries a penalty of 20 years to life. It is probable here, however, that the psychotic episodes will recur and that, eventually, they will necessitate a transfer to Dannemora State Hospital which houses prisoners who become mentally ill following sentence.

Psychotic reactions in post-traumatic cases are almost invariably episodic. Their ultimate outcome, at this time, must be accepted as relatively unpredictable.

17

He did it just for kicks

"I don't know why I shot her; the urge just came over me," Andrew Polo sobbed to police in West Milford, where he was held without bail on a charge of assault with intent to kill.

NEWS, 9/11/56

ON OCCASION, I have encountered murderers suffering from organic brain disease where there was no history of trauma. One of the first that I saw was an epileptic who had killed his mother while in a post-convulsive clouded state. Ostensibly he had no recollection of the matricide. Another was afflicted with cerebral arteriosclerosis, a hardening of the blood vessels supplying the brain. He bludgeoned an innocent victim, believing that the person was instrumental in depriving him of his already waning potency. A third, suffering from brain syphilis, shot his wife after castrating himself.

During the past year, I was retained to examine a male, aged 20, who had slain his girl friend without apparent provocation. The crime had occurred in a neighboring state. My investigations revealed that he had been seeing this girl regularly for two years and that there had never been any infidelity on the part of either.

Early one evening, he took her out for a ride in his car. This was evidently a customary practice. There were no eye-witnesses of the murder. The prosecutor, counsel for defense, and I were all obliged to piece together fragmentarily, the demonstrable facts. The defendant gave us no idea as to why he had killed.

Immediately following the murder, according to his father, he had come home and inquired quite casually whether there was any coffee. He then slept soundly for two and a half hours. At this time, the police arrived. He greeted them as though nothing had happened. When they inquired about the whereabouts of his girl friend, he said that he had been with her all day and that when he last saw her she was in a Plymouth car with two other fellows.

Ironically enough, the defendant had made a public announcement of his betrothal to the deceased earlier that same day. He readily admitted the murder, though. His reason was simply, "It was one of those things." He discussed the tragedy in an unconcerned, if not casual manner. But he was vexed no end over having been awakened by the Police at 2 A.M.

I interviewed him for several hours at the County Prison. From the beginning, it was evident to me that he was psychotic—though, as in so many cases, malingering was suspected.

Upon entering the examining room, he exhibited an unmistakably hostile attitude. He glowered at me before I asked him a question. His answers were surly and snarling. Even those he gave in response to inquiries about statistical data were invariably truculent. Yet everything he said was coherent, as the following reportorial quotations demonstrate:

(Name?) A. *P.* As to siblings, he stated that he had two brothers, 26 and 24. (This was verified.) When questioned about his relations with them, he replied: *They never did make any difference to me.* (What about friends?) *Never had none.* (Parents?) *They were no bargain, either. At 16 I started to take off to Mexico, got only as far as Baltimore—money gave out.* (Girl friend?) *She's still around.* (But it is said that you shot her). *Maybe I did—maybe it just happened.* (Were you not engaged to marry her?) *Yeah, in a couple of weeks.* (Then why kill her?) *Just for a kick.* (Had feelings like killing before?) *Yeah, I used to cut guys.* (Why?) *Anybody that crossed me, I'd like to kill 'em.* He then laughed fiendishly when describing a bleeding victim whom he had slashed. (Why carry a knife or gun?) *For protection. Twice when I passed the park, somebody took a shot at me.* (He could not identify the assailants). *I'm not worried—I can always take care of myself.* (Do you think about the consequences of the crime of which you are accused?) *I know this—if I've got to go to a nut-house on a second degree murder rap, I'd get a . . . machine gun and kill about 50 people. If I had a chance to go to the chair, I'd grab at it.*

Present at the interview were two other psychiatrists and the attorney defending the accused. When reminded of the fact that his father had arranged for our services in his behalf, he retorted, "None of you are any good—I didn't want anybody to help me. I told you before I don't give a goddam what happens."

The day following this session, I interviewed his father, mother, brother, and sister. The relatives were unanimous in their convictions that the defendant had been "normal" and sociable prior to the onset of an attack of chorea at the age of 13. This neurological disease, alluded to in common parlance as St. Vitus dance, is characterized by involuntary tremors of the limbs and twitches of the head and facial musculature. Medical science now knows that the disturbance is connected with changes in the sub-brain, i.e., the parasympathetic system which has to do with emotion rather than intellectual functioning.

In the case of this defendant, we were concerned with a person who, prior to the organic upset at the age of 13, had existed in a state of comparative calm. It was only afterwards that he began to show the definite mental changes. He became irascible and suspicious even of his relatives. He accused his sister and his brother of "snooping" on him. He launched an unprovoked assault upon the brother. He had also developed the habit of foully reviling drivers who passed him in ordinary traffic. According to his brother, he actually tried to run cars down on the highway if they tried to pass him. "He would threaten and curse them and one time he offered to knock a fellow's brains out."

A few days later, I again interviewed the defendant, this time to ask him if he wished to change any of the statements he had made to me. Some of his replies follow:

Q. *Do you want to make any changes in your remarks made to me in connection with the alleged crime?* A. No.

Q. *Why did you kill your girl friend?* A. *Just for a kick.*

Q. *Why did you try to assault your brother?* A. *Just for a kick, one of those things.*

Q. *Why did you deliberately smash a car?* A. *Just got mad. Don't like things to get the best of me.*

About a car-smashing incident, his father said:

"There was a minor defect in the fuel pump. In a rage, he attempted to break the car apart with a wrench, shrieking that the bastards, that is, the auto workers, didn't know anything."

Later, the defendant repeated his hate feelings. He expostulated: "Even if I get out tomorrow, I'll kill that f . . . uncle of C. (the deceased)." Just what connotation this threat carried, I was unable to perceive. Nor could his relatives understand it.

The defendant stated further: "If anybody bothers me, I'll do the first thing that comes to my mind."

Then again, in reference to his brother, he shouted: "F . . . him! He ain't never done me no favors."

Three other psychiatrists and I testified that the organic brain pathology (the chorea) had so distorted his judgment as to make him irresponsible for his acts. A psychiatrist for the state regarded him as only "a psychopath"—a bad boy. On the witness stand, I called attention to the fact that all of his anti-social propensities had erupted after the onset of the brain disorder. This had affected his reservoir of emotivity. The belligerence he thereafter displayed was directed even against those he had formerly regarded as friends. Primitive hate had been unloosed in him by the damage involving the emotional centers of the brain.

A board of 3 or 5 psychiatrists could have drawn conclusions in this case on a strictly scientific level. It is not easy to explain adequately such medical technicalities to a lay jury. This particular jury, however, decided to absolve the defendant of culpability on the grounds of his mental illness. He was committed to a state hospital for the criminally insane.

18 The compulsion to dominate

A 25 year-old Brooklyn furniture repairman, father of two children, was booked on a homicide charge at 1:44 a.m. today in the brutal murder of Ann Yarrow on February 6. . . . Besides the homicide count, Farrell also was booked on four other charges—assault, robbery, rape and violation of the weapons law.

NEW YORK TIMES, 3/2/55

SOMETIMES, though not often, we meet a murderer whose psychological processes do not fit neatly into any one of the categories described in the official nomenclature. His reactions and performance may be motivated by elements stemming from a confusion of aberrations, and occasionally from environmental influences, as well. The following is a case in point.

An indictment for the crime of murder in the first degree was filed against James Patrick Farrell in March 1955. Allegedly, he had followed a girl whom he had never seen before to her living quarters in the Greenwich Village section of New York. Thereafter, it was contended by the police and the District Attorney, he had raped her, mutilated her, and finally killed her by stabbing.

Prior to the killing, he had been apprehended for the attempted rape of his sister-in-law. The investigation of this assault led to other clues which ultimately connected him with the subsequent murder. When the accusation was made, he confessed to guilt in both crimes.

The possibility of distorted mentality needed to be examined. I tried to trace the behavior patterns to their incipient sources and to follow them through their later metamorphoses in such a manner as to throw some light upon the criminal motivation.

At the very outset of the investigation, I realized that the defendant might have ample reason to harbor an anti-social attitude about his mother, in particular, and about society, in general. He was born an out-of-wedlock child. He later learned that he had been born in prison, that his mother had been sent there on a prostitution charge. His rearing, from early childhood up to the age of 16, had been in foster homes and foundling institutions.

In this case I was fortunate in being afforded access to a wealth of historical material which proved most helpful in fathoming the nature of the ensuing psychopathology. The informative sources included the mother, the sister-in-law, whom he had attacked, two arresting officers and the defendant himself. He spoke freely and with apparent frankness to the officers and the examiners.

According to the mother, he began to act peculiarly shortly after entering school.

He would remain alone and sulk and once or twice he burnt his school books down in the cellar. My father told him to go out and play cops and robbers with the other kids, but he would stick around listening to the women talking. When he was around 9 or 10, he got a book about sex. He always wanted to read it. He always seemed to know everything about the opposite sex. . . . Later, one of his foster mothers had him sent to Warwick (a state school for pre-adolescent delinquents). (Why?)

He had destroyed the daughter's clothing. Then he went to the movies and hid there. Shortly after, broken glass was found in a salad bowl from which the family was served. He ascribed this to the accidental slamming of a door to the icebox. When he went to the movies, he usually had no money. He said that a man there gave him a few dollars. Then he said he started out on the way to look for easy money along these lines. (Did you know anything about his sexual abnormality?) *Yes. When he came out of Warwick, Mr. C., a probation officer, asked me if I would take him home with me. So I had my husband* (the mother had, by this time, been married and felt she could have him live with her) *go and bring him. One night, my husband was working. Then he mentioned that a woman in a hospital had told him about his background and me. He said that she asked him why I had to live with a man like my husband when a nice looking fellow like him was around the house.* (Age of son at that time?) *About 16. Mr. C., the probation officer, then placed him nearby with a foster couple. In 2 days, the new foster mother told her husband that she wants to get rid of him. When my boy called me on the phone I asked him what had happened. He said that he had felt a desire to attack the woman and knock her out. The husband sent him back to Mr. C. Then, all of a sudden, he married an older woman, knowing that she was already pregnant by another man. He said he loved her anyway, that he felt it was the decent thing to give the child a name.*

After living with the newly acquired wife, he visited his mother frequently. From her account, there was something extra-filial in his interpretation of their relationship. He recalled that a woman psychiatrist had asked him "Would you like to go to bed with your mother?" This question, he reported, so enraged him that he wanted to "hit her with a swivel chair." He apparently thought better of it, however, as he continued his visit to his mother. She went on with her story.

"Though he was married, he was also living with some fellow in Greenwich Village. The fellow he roomed with came over. He said 'I don't mind him coming to live with me, but I don't like what he says.' I said 'What do you mean?' He said, 'He is going to kill your daughter' (his half-sister, the issue of a legitimate wedlock). I said 'What did she ever do to him?' He just shook his head. My son later said the fellow was lying."

One Saturday I was lying down inside the room. He knocked on the door and asked me if he could talk to me. He said 'If you knew what was on my mind you wouldn't want me here any more.' I thought maybe he wanted to do some damage to us. He then said 'I was in there taking a shower just now and I had the desire to come out here and without my clothes on.' I told him that anybody that thought like that must have a sick mind. Then he told me about reading a book once where a fellow was jealous of his father and wanted to make love to his mother. He came back a few weeks later and said 'You'll never know if you don't give me that affection. It will bring me out of my present frame of mind.' I asked him what he was referring to. He then said 'The desire to hurt people.' (Then what occurred?) *I am ashamed to say. . . . There was a belt laying on a chair. He said he had a desire to hit me with it; that he wanted to see welts all over my body. . . . Then he told me about some pictures he was drawing. One was the picture of a woman. They were roasting her like a pig and pouring gravy all over her body. He was going to title that one "The Last Supper." Another was the picture of a nun. She had a baby dragging from her breast and she had no clothes on. There was another fellow behind her, horse-whipping her.*

The mechanisms of symbology evolved thus far are obvious. Much more was to come, however.

The police had obtained very complete statements from the defendants both about his crimes and his past. The account given by Detective Henry Murcia is here repeated verbatim:

It was on March 1, 1955, about 11:30 A.M. *at the 9th Squad Detective office. The defendant had just seated himself in a chair. His very first words were "I wish I had been shot." I said "Why do you feel that way? Is it because of what happened to your sister-in-law?" "No, that is not it, I really didn't mean to hurt her."*

I am Detective Murcia. If you tell the truth here you will be able to help yourself out, if there is anything on your mind. Then he said:

"I've had tough breaks since the day I was born. I found out that I was born in a prison. My mother was arrested for prostitution a couple of times and on one of those occasions I was born in prison."

What seemed to bother you after that? "I went to live with foster parents. Before that, my mother used to tell me dirty jokes and later on even made unnatural advances towards me. . . . When I was out with foster parents in Queens, one day they said I socked a girl with a bat. I don't know what got into me after that, but I broke up my foster parents' apartment. The father said I made a shambles of the place. I slammed the door to the ice-box and I believe glass shattered on the peaches and they accused me of putting ground glass in their food."

At this point in his life, the defendant was sent to Warwick. While there, he yielded to homosexual advances of other inmates, usually by passive pederasty. As a result of these practices, arrangements were made for his admission to the camp of Dr. Henry, a specialist in the treatment of sexual abnormality. (His recent book "Sex Variants" was indeed a commendable contribution to the literature dealing with sexual psychopathy.) Though the defendant had one experience there, the doctor's efforts at rehabilitation proved helpful, since he was accepted for army service shortly thereafter. Seemingly, he adjusted satisfactorily in Korea. But when he came home on furlough, he did a very strange thing. Detective Murcia's report continues:

Q. *What happened when you came home on leave?* A. *I met Marilyn.*

Q. *Who is Marilyn?* A. *Marilyn is my wife. We got married, and she left me on the wedding night, and took off with some old bastard named S. from California. In the four years that I was away—she had two children by him.*

Q. *I thought you had been separated four years.* A. *I wrote her while I was away.*

Q. *Are these children with you now?* A. *Yes, but the child she is expecting now is mine. At the time Marilyn and that old bastard had broken up. We spoke a few times and got together again. I believe she had been paying my mother to take care of the children.*

Q. *How about your sexual relationships?* A. *They have been more than sufficient.*

Q. *What do you mean by that?* (He then described to the officer a variety of perversions which they practiced in addition to normal coitus and continued his answer.) A. *I had been getting an urge to hurt. My stomach would go up and down. . . . It is a funny thing, I never had any sex feeling toward my sister-in-law. The day before it happened* (the stabbing), *I took a kitchen knife from my wife without her knowledge. She was looking for it, and meanwhile I had hidden it between my belt and trousers. . . . Then I began to think about the French war bride who lived across the hall—I got the urge to cut her up* (he gained entrance upon the pretext of buying her bed, but discovered her boy on it, and then departed). *I then started to think of my sister-in-law. I went down to her house on 4th Street and a Jew bastard who used to be my wife's stepfather was in the apartment. I know that she hasn't got a husband and that her child is illegitimate. I knew he paid for her clothes* (*did certain things with her indicating cunnilingus*). *She had told me that a girl could make a lot of money that way. I made him sit on the floor. I told her to take off her clothes. She refused. I ripped off her bra and threw her on the bed. I held the knife at her back. I told the Jew to get the hell out. I'd just gotten started when I heard the cops. I threw the knife and went down the fire escape.*

The sister-in-law was unable to explain his tempestuous performances. She stated that she had known him only casually both before and after his marriage to her sister. "He used to come over once in a while alone. He seemed to be all right to me. She knew nothing about the destructive things he had done. She also denied that he had ever accused her of having anything to do with the man whom the defendant had alluded to as a "Jew bastard."

(Just before being cornered, it was reported by another officer that the defendant had defied the officers to shoot him. The same patrolman stated that in no other way did he act or talk irrationally and showed no signs of fear or panic.)

The assault just described occurred several days after the murder.

The statements that follow now are concerned solely with the murder case:

I'm going to tell you everything. I left my house on a Saturday. That is the day my mother-in-law comes over. . . . I had the urge to hurt. I went to the Village from Brooklyn. I bought the knife at a cripple shop on 8th Street. I stood on the corner watching people go by. A girl passed by. She was wearing dungarees. I don't remember whether she smiled at me or not, but I do know that the pants attracted me. . . . I followed her. She was going east on 8th Street toward 3rd Avenue. She crossed 5th Avenue and I crossed behind her to her apartment on 3rd Avenue and East 4th Street. I used to live on East 3rd when it was a YMCA. *I believe she knew I followed her by the way she looked at me. . . . When she got in I knocked on the door. She opened it partially. I pushed in with my shoulder and went in. I touched her on the shoulder and she said don't hurt her. She started to get excited and the more excited she got, the more panting urge I got. I grabbed her by the throat with my left hand and squeezed.—As she seemed to lose consciousness I then took the knife. I hit her twice with it and she went down. I don't know if it was on a bed or a mattress.—I took her dungarees off and threw them on the side.—I pulled a white blouse or a sweater she had on above her breasts. I placed a pillow under her* (buttocks). *I usually prop them up that way.—I ripped the rag off* (presumably a Kotex). *I had intercourse with her. I stabbed her a few more times around the chest. Then I put the knife in her* (vagina) *with a twist and then wiped it off on a towel.—Then I left the apartment and walked down the street toward East Houston and I believe I threw the knife away on the way to the subway in one of the sewers.*

When he finally confessed, he said he was glad he had been caught. His statements never struck me as being fabrications because the details which we already know, were never told or published.

All of the officers described the defendant as calm and matter-of-fact in discussing the crime. They were amazed, however, by his sense of guilt regarding a homosexual experience with a colored man just prior to the murder; this, despite his many previous excursions into this area of behavior.

The defendant was under constant observation at the hospital for one month and three days. The nurses' notes fail to indicate any anti-social tendencies, sexual or otherwise. Similarly, he was at all times cooperative in the psychiatric and psychological examinations conducted singly and in conference by five senior staff members. Physically, there were no demonstrable abnormalities. The psychiatric testing revealed a dull normal intelligence. Despite these negative findings, the defendant displayed at all times an obtuseness towards accepted moral requirements. They apparently did not register upon his consciousness, either emotionally or intellectually.

This kind of calloused reaction is usually called "psychopathic personality" and is regarded as an inborn or innate psychological distortion. Though the defendant's reaction bears all the major earmarks of this disorder, I am not at all convinced that the tendencies in his case were either fundamental or irremediable. It is relatively certain that he did not begin to display any anti-social behavior prior to being made conscious of what he considered his ignominy, i.e., his illegitimacy and prison birth. It was then that his hatred erupted into acts of murderous proportions and that the sadistic fantasies, crudely sublimated in pictorial form, began.

Here is a sampling of his answers:

Q. *In our numerous interviews with you, there were quite a number of things that happened that seemed rather unusual. In the first place, you were raised in foster homes. Were you particularly unhappy over that?* A. *A bit confused because of rapid changes in environment.*

Q. *Did you harbor resentment toward your mother?* A. *It is quite possible that I did hold her responsible.*

Q. *Hatred of her?* A. *That's possible. My emotions concerning her are mixed.*

Q. *Will you be a little more explicit?* A. *When I was* 12 *or* 13 *I wanted her.*

Q. *What made you change?* A. *I was disappointed by the fact that she wasn't the woman I thought she was. I learned that I was illegitimate.*

Q. *You mentioned assaulting an older woman when you were about* 14. *Did you have a feeling of wanting to have intercourse with her?* A. *Yes.*

Q. *Why didn't you approach her rather than committing assault?* A. *I don't know.*

Q. *On one occasion you tore up a woman's clothes. She lived in the same foster home with you?* A. *She was the* daughter of my foster mother. She met a fellow and groomed him to be her husband. Before they could go through with it, he was inducted in the Army. He had an accident and his leg had to be amputated. When he returned home, she wouldn't allow him in. She wanted someone with both their legs. Her boss had a date with her that night and brought her candy and flowers. I felt if she couldn't dress to go out with him, that would be the end of the date. I took a knife and cut up her clothes and left the house.

Q. After you attacked your sister-in-law and on other occasions, you expressed a desire to be shot? A. Being unfaithful to my wife is bad enough, but slipping into homosexuality is much worse.

Q. Why tendencies to attack women? A. I have a great deal of pride for myself.

Q. When you began to indulge in homosexual practices, were you the active or the passive party? A. That's what I can't understand. My very earliest experience was an aggressor, and all subsequent exchange was of a passive nature.

Q. In your crimes, then, you felt like you were again the aggressor? A. Yes, it is better to be a creator than a victim.

Q. You feel guilt concerning infidelity to your wife despite the fact that your wife had borne two illegitimate children after you had married her? A. You can't possibly convict someone of something they did when they were young and foolish.

Q. I still don't see how the enormity of criminal impli-

cation in homosexual relationship could prompt one to want to be killed for it? A. *Perhaps I can explain it this way. I realized my attraction to my wife rested on the fact that she is aggressive, and looks a bit like me physically, which is a male tendency. I recognized that in her. When I had aggressive homosexual feelings, I recognized that it would be the male in her.*

Q. *Then it seems to follow that in your rather strenuous sexual performance with her, you were the dominant figure, at least momentarily?* A. *I believe that answers it.*

Betraying further his feeble efforts to compensate for his unconscious feelings of sexual inadequacy, he described a painting he had made before he went into the Army. It was of a nude woman with a sword piercing her vagina and coming out at the nape of her neck. He captioned it "Virility."

I feel definitely that the train of symptoms in this case can be considered a hodgepodge of psychopathological manifestations. The sociopathic elements are in the majority. But the schizoid and psychoneurotic traits are also readily discernible. The sudden uncontrollable urges to assault and murder are more characteristic of violent compulsions than they are of the mere anti-social rebellions of the sociopath, usually perpetrated on the conscious level. The weird environmental factors can account for a good deal of the symptomatology. The lack of appropriate emotivity, however, is frequently indicative of the more malignant mental disorder of schizophrenia. But no delusions or hallucinatory phenomena were observable. It is quite possible that had the familial set-up in this case been a stable one, we would not now have a murderer confronting us. Of one thing, I am certain—there are too many symptoms atypical of the sociopath to include this defendant in that category.

19

The larger goal

THE PHILOSOPHERS through the centuries have stressed that the level of any successful society is reflected in the understanding and relationship of the private citizen to the laws which he has agreed are to govern him. With these basic factors in view, the cases presented have emphasized the *purpose* of judgment and penalty rather than judgment and penalty as separated actions.

It is hoped that the material in the body of this book will serve to provide the average citizen as well as the public servant with a more balanced view of the responsibilities of those persons who represent the public interests in the judgment, prosecution, and prevention of murder. It is also hoped that the reader will obtain a view of the many different legal processes which are employed to protect and extend his social safety.

A greater awareness of the *quality* of murder can help our society to deal more understandingly with the criminal who, although guilty of a destructive act, nevertheless may not be physically or morally responsible because of severe mental illness. In following this course, it is not necessary in any way to pamper or explain away the actions of the destructive criminal whose vicious acts must be punished to the full extent of existing law.

The awareness of the *quality* of any criminal act can lead us to the stage where we may decide with greater assurance whether our society is better served when a psychotic, found guilty of committing a crime, is to be judged and punished according to the same rules which apply to the vicious social criminal; or, when he is committed to a mental institution (out of harm's way and, in most instances, for a period of longer duration), where his condition can be treated and where his behavior can be studied. The knowledge from that study can then be applied to the major function of the legal process, which is, in essence, the prevention of crime.

In actual practice, we have come a long way towards a more human approach in the judgment of the mentally ill criminal. The M'Naughton Rules (knowledge of right and wrong) are still adhered to in the greater part of the United States, in the British Commonwealth, and in many other sections of the world. Medical opinion, however, is now sought more and more frequently, though in the main, the verdict of judge and jury still conforms to the M'Naughton Rules.

In several areas of the United States, genuine efforts have been made to improve the standards of judging the culpability of mentally ill accused of having committed a capital offense. For example, the state of Massachusetts passed the Briggs Law, in 1921, authorizing the designation of a permanent psychiatric panel to examine all criminals charged with murder. The doctors so chosen are selected by the State Mental Health Department. When a defendant is found suffering from severe mental illness, he is automatically committed to a psychiatric institution. The recommendations of the panel are almost invariably accepted by the courts and the prosecution. No questions are raised as to the defendant's ability to "know right from wrong," in the accepted sense, once the doctors have decided that he is a victim of severe mental illness.

Advances have also been made in New York State where, in 1939, the Desmond Act was passed, decreeing that the defendant must have the capability of understanding the charges and therefore be equal to making a proper defense. As in the Massachusetts reform, the defendant is examined routinely at the Court of General Sessions by qualified psychiatrists of the Department of Hospitals. Rarely does there arise a controversy regarding these findings.

In Europe, the modern approach inclines towards the more scientific, with emphasis placed on the psychiatric rather than the strictly legal consideration. For example, the Copenhagen approach entirely overrides the M'Naughton precepts, and gives primary consideration to the psychiatric evaluation. In that city, a special institution under the administrative control of the police and under the medical control of a psychiatrist, assisted by three other mental specialists, has been established. The criminal is placed here immediately after the crime. Joint examinations are held in the office of the chief psychiatrist regularly, over a period of two weeks to three months. The decisions of the institution doctors are then submitted to a Board of Forensic Medicine presided over by the professor of psychiatry at the University of Copenhagen. The conclusions of the Board are invariably endorsed by the court, which accepts such medical findings as final.

Similarly in the Netherlands, the defendant is examined both mentally and physically in the prison after arrest. If mental complications are suspected, the defendant is referred to the Clinic at Utrecht for further appraisal by psychiatrists, psychologists, and social workers. The court makes its decision solely on the basis of the professional medical and psychological opinion.

In Spain and Italy, mental examinations are conducted at the discretion of the magistrates who select the psychiatrists (unfortunately) without proper regard to qualifications. But the psychiatric opinions are given major consideration.

The cooperation between psychiatry and law is ever increasing. It presages a period when what has formerly been considered the unknown and the fearful in human behavior will be understood and will no longer act as a threat.

The old Biblical judgment of an eye for an eye and a tooth for a tooth becomes meaningful only when we understand that it was born out of the need to advance a productive society. Today that interest is best expressed when the administration of justice is not separated from the larger goal: the prevention of further criminal acts.